D0042060

Listen To The Millrace

LISTEN TO
THE MILLRACE

by BARTON PORTER

Paintings by Mike Casad

M. J. STONE COMPANY

COPYRIGHT © 1978 BY BARTON PORTER

ALL RIGHTS RESERVED INCLUDING THE RIGHT

TO REPRODUCE THIS BOOK OR PARTS THEREOF IN ANY FORM

LIBRARY OF CONGRESS CATALOG CARD NUMBER: 78-66449

ISBN: 0-9601888-0-0

M. J. STONE COMPANY

P.O. BOX 12793

SEATTLE, WASHINGTON 98111

For my grandchildren
Casey
Heidi
Barry
Amy

CONTENTS

Chapter 1

THIS REMINDS ME

This is the first time in many years that I've driven over this old wagon road. These summer-browned rolling hills edged with tall green pines and autumn-yellowed poplars make a picture familiar to me since I was a boy. It now reminds me that the ones who made this valley home for me to keep coming back to are gone away, even as those freshly painted leaves soon too shall go.

Now, over there is the Milwaukee Railroad that Walter and I left on right after I finished high school. No one else was in my class so the graduation exercise was cancelled when I got sick. Good-bye time at our front door that morning had me all choked up. But I wanted to show I was up to living in the city as well as in the country, and expected it would make me feel as superior as certain city people had been with me. Leaving home was not new to Walter. His dad was railroad section foreman and he rode on a pass, but I had to pay. The Milwaukee was electrified and only ten years old then. All the way into Seattle there was one thing after another to make me sit up and take notice. After we got off the train and walked a few blocks from the depot, Walter nudged me and pointed up. I still see, as close beside me as then, all those famed forty-two stories of the L. C. Smith Building piled up into the sky. Walter had a room with board two miles away where I could stay. Riding a streetcar to it was new excitement for me and only cost a nickel. The next day I got a job filling orders in a big wholesale hardware establishment. It paid fifteen dollars for a forty-eight hour week. A lot of years have passed since then.

After driving a hundred miles today I'm getting near Thorp Prairie. The big firs and pines that grew along here went to the sawmill a long time ago. Horseshoe Canyon here reminds me of one time when the Thorp High School basketball team rode in Archie Hornpole's bobsled over this road packed with snow twenty-two miles to Roslyn. Archie probably got two bits a head for all six of us and it would've cost twice that much riding on cushions in a warm railroad car. We weren't much of a drag on Archie's poor old horses, as most of the way we walked or ran behind his bobsled to keep from freezing. There was a layer of straw in the bobsled box that, cold as it was, made a soft place to sit till we caught our wind and could run another mile. We got to Roslyn long after dark, cold, tired and hungry — not much good against a team that had just come from resting after supper in warm homes. I never did know the score and I was then too numb to care.

This trip is nothing like that one. There's the two-room unpainted house where Dave Madog, who was Welsh, lived as a bachelor. In this desert climate a house has little need of paint. Dave hauled his water two miles from Taneum Creek and must have boiled it for drinking. When I was in the first grade he rescued me from a long ride, to say the least, on Bill Garver's pony. It was after school and the minute Bill boosted me up into the saddle his pony took off for home — three miles distant. All I knew was to clutch the saddle horn and hang on. Then, at the turn of the street, Dave stepped in front of the pony and I slid off in a hurry.

There, still rusting away inside that barbed wire fence, is the Milwaukee grain binder that my dad sold Dave. It cut the ripened stems of grain and tied them with Manila twine into armload-sized bundles that were hauled on a wagon to near the barn and stacked twelve feet high. Before the end of September they were fed into what was to me a miraculous threshing machine powered by a leviathan steam tractor. I thought it was the biggest and most amazing piece of machinery in the world. Even that grain binder was a wonder of my world. There's little of that red or green paint left on it now. The wood tongue is gone, used for firewood maybe. And just think, when drawn by three strong horses that binder wrapped up ten or so acres of tall golden wheat stems in a day. Now it is overgrown with weeds and not worth hauling away for junk.

I learned who lived on these farms by riding up here with my dad in our buggy. That was a treat for us boys. Besides grain binders, my dad sold wagons, hay rakes, cream separators, harrows, and every other kind of farm equipment to farmers who lived near Thorp.

That's the school back there, and here's the abandoned house Dobie Shaw built before I was born. He dug and drove a two-inch pipe a long way down so he could draw up water with a pitcher pump. After a lifetime of growing spuds and grain, while raising children on this dry windswept land, he and his wife quit and moved to Thorp where he, at least, took it easy. Always ready to joke, Dobie and I had many a laugh together.

It's about a mile over that hill to the Taneum Canyon where I worked in a sawmill the summers I was sixteen and seventeen. The hours were half again as long as now. Our foreman wanted everyone to know how apt his ten-year-old son was with machinery, so in proof of that one afternoon he had the boy feeding the band resaw. Working nearby, I was startled to hear yelling and rushed to him. It horrified me to see his arm between the rollers, moving toward the saw. I pulled on his arm as I stepped on the foot pedal to spread the steel rollers. But the pedal would not go down, for he had put a block of wood underneath it to stand on. And the rollers would not stop turning! Oh, that I'd never heard and had to see what that saw did. The desperate father rushed up and seized the saw's back edge with his bare hands in vain to stop it. If I'd only known, I could have stopped the rollers by shoving a piece of board between the cogs. I walked the seven miles home that afternoon and never went back.

It's a few miles from here to the cemetery where my parents are buried. I'll stop there before going on to Thorp. In this streamlined car it doesn't take long. Now there already is the cemetery gate. I'll park here next to the fence. I see two stones raised for neighboring pioneers who hated each other a lot. Neither one ever dreamed they'd be as close together as they are now. Some stones in here were familiar to me even before I could read the names and dates on them. Now when I read them along with others put here afterward it brings those faces and voices back to life for me. Here in this corner is the flat stone for my parents, showing they were on this earth an average of ninety-one years.

At this back edge of the cemetery is a clear view of Thorp where we lived all my boyhood. The millpond is down there and near it the tall flour mill is standing. There is no sign of the sawmill or of the light plant which once stood just across the falls from the flour mill. Beyond the mills was the pond where I worked one winter loading railroad boxcars with foot-thick ice.

I see they took the bell out, then cut the steeple off the Methodist church. And I hear they now hold dances there. Shades of Saint Matthew! . . . That schoolhouse looks modern. The one I went to looked modern to us, but it's gone. So are the Taneum House and the Odd Fellows Hall above Brain's store. Those buildings the five saloons were in are gone, too. Fire had its way. But in memory I still see the open back door of Tim's Place there. Ladies who took care of their reputations didn't enter the back door or the front door of saloons, so if one ever wanted beer it had to be passed out that back door in a lard pail and carried home. Of all those old business buildings only our old store stands. My brother (he calls himself "Ol' Charlie" now) still lives there beside it. One block this way I see his little honey-extracting house where one year he packed 32,000 pounds of honey. The depot was bought by a man "born and raised" in it, who moved it down across the road to his place. But the old livery stable is still there near where our swimming hole was. Below that nearby wooden bridge is a meadow of white clover. After our swim on a hot afternoon, we went there to lie in the shade and listen to the millrace rippling over its rock-strewn bed. Down near those woods to my right is where the slaughterhouse stood. It was a handy place for our dog Major to find a steer's shinbone to bring and gnaw on in our front yard.

Ellensburg, the county seat, is down the river about eight miles from here where that smoke is. A month before I was out of high school I joined the state militia there during the First World War. One summer evening after drill as I walked along Pearl Street at dusk, I heard an unusual honking approaching. Soon five or six automobiles with lights on and tops down drove up and stopped at the intersection. The drivers and all who sat in them were masked and robed. However, perched high on top of one back seat was a bare-headed, undisguised man with his hands fastened behind his back. Placards hanging from his neck read: GOOD NEWS, GERMANY IS WINNING.

The honking continued until a crowd gathered. I kept at the outer edge. There were threats to use a rope. Then, above the threats and hoots, I heard the mob's victim ask for a chance to say something. "Why not let him talk," some brave ones conceded, "before we hang him."

It then got quiet enough for me to clearly hear these words spoken in a calm voice:

"I've got a wife and six kids and my mother to support but I'll go tomorrow and join the army with any of you. Most of you are more able to go than I am. Some of your wives are schoolteachers. Mr. Parker here [the pinioned man nodded to his left], the revered principal of our high school, is one. His wife made the boast in public —"

Suddenly a masked man jumped up and drove his fist into the face of the defenseless man, knocking him back onto the folded-down auto top. More blows fell. Then I recognized a tall man pushing through the crowd to the shame-ridden automobile. I'd heard he taught history at Broadway High School in Seattle and that his wife was also a teacher. They lived on a farm near Thorp in the summer. But now it made me sick to see him in affectation of patriotism rain blows on the bound and downed, courageous father's head and face. The automobiles, as though ashamed and wanting to hide, moved on with their mob of masked creatures and their captive.

In the next day's edition of the *Ellensburg Evening Record* I read in essence the following: "Yesterday evening a group of citizens brought an agitator from Kittitas into Ellensburg. They took him out to the edge of town and, after warning him to behave, released him." That is all I ever read about that evening's disgrace. However, I heard that the "agitator" was Irish and so wanted the English beaten by the Germans or anyone else. Whatever the reason, I've never seen such bravery on the one hand, nor such cowardice on the other, as was shown at Fourth and Pearl in Ellensburg that evening in June.

Ten years before that spectacle taught me what a dastardly cloak patriotism could wear, I had one of the happiest moments of my boyhood, only two miles from here. It was there beside the river at the Burns place when I got Buster. I can see it now. I'd heard that Burns had a litter of pups for sale at fifty cents each so I began a campaign at home to get one. At the time we were down to only Major, giving my parents an excuse to say yes. On the very next Saturday morning I was walking down that road holding a fifty-cent piece that would give me the pick of several newly weaned pups. They had long black hair, and I chose one with brown and white on head and feet because he made friends with me. I took him in my arms and began my two-mile walk home. It was easy to whistle. When I got out to that main road I met Henry Parr driving his wagon to Thorp. I remember the way he smiled as he stopped his team and invited me to ride.

It was a joy having a pup to love. When Buster grew up he liked to wear a harness and pull our wagon or sled. In summer when we dove in the swimming hole, he jumped in right on top of us. In winter he was happy to run between my legs, pulling me on ice skates. He came and waited for us to get out of school. One night he was tempted to roam and got in range of a shotgun that perforated his front paw. I watched anxiously, wondering whether the shot would ever come out or what. But at last he walked without a limp again.

The summer that I went to work in the mill, Buster got so sick he could hardly walk. He died on a hot Sunday morning when I was home. I can see our old house there now. We were at the table enjoying the biscuits my mother always tried to make for Sunday breakfast, when some noise caused my brother to go out. He had several beehives in the chicken yard and the gate had been left open. He called me to come and get my dog, but before there was time for that he had carried Buster away from the beehives. We all hurried out and I'll never forget seeing Buster laid on the ground whimpering. He was just covered with buzzing, stinging bees. Using the best tool handy my dad ended Buster's suffering with one merciful blow. My brother was stung so many times by the mad bees that the doctor was called. We buried Buster on the other side of the swimming hole near that tall pine tree.

No other place could bring up the memories in me that this one does. Down there is where my parents and the friends of my boyhood lived. How I wish they were still there. But up here is where burial prayers and tearful good-byes have already been said for most of them. I would like to tell what I remember of them and of life in that tiny village when I was about eight and all my friends called me Chub.

Chapter 2

THE KITTITAS BREEZE

We lived in Thorp on the east slope of the North Cascades where Mount Stuart's snowy granite peak shone down on us from thirty miles away. A few white clouds floating near the peak early on a spring morning meant the relentless northwest wind would blow all day, and might blow steadily for a month or more. Then people would wonder what had possessed their neighbor John Newman in 1890 to plan for a village four blocks square, expecting them to live in it. But quite as much as that Kittitas *breeze* was denounced in the spring, it was welcomed on many a hot summer afternoon. And Thorp always to me was the only place for a boy to have fun. It was in the narrow upper end of a valley crowded with lush alfalfa hay meadows and fields heavy with wheat, oats and barley. Our home there was in six small rooms adjoining a long, narrow dry goods, shoe and hardware store with candy, tobacco and drug departments in it.

Across the street was the red depot of the Northern Pacific Railroad where its agent lived with his family. Often I peeked in the window at him tapping his *rat-tat-tat* on the telegraph key. Atop a tall pole above the lookout bay window were two signal arms that the agent pointed to the sky or sideways by shifting two heavy iron levers. They told the train engineer to stop or to keep on going. When the noon train rolled in with the baggage door open, the agent pulled his four-wheeled truck bumping over the worn splintery platform to it. The iron-tired truck sometimes was loaded with five-gallon cans of cream and boxes of fruit with a bulky breadbasket on top.

Painted in big white letters on each end of the depot was the word THORP. Even after our family moved there in the early 1900s when I was two, the population stayed at about two hundred. With that name it could hardly have hoped to grow much bigger, since a thorp always was a small agricultural community. Six hundred years ago Chaucer spelled it "thrope." In Thorp we had no "right" side of the railroad track. Instead, there were two sides, and so few lived on either side that we were as glad to know those from the one side as those from the other.

A mile north of Thorp ran the swift Yakima River that in some years flooded the bottom land all the way to our house. Protecting us from the river's destructive current, though, were woods of willow, chokecherry, serviceberry and other bushes rooted down among the rugged white aspens and virgin pitch-seeping pines. The woods bordered open spaces of white clover pasture where horses from the livery stable or cows and sheep grazed near the millrace. In other directions there were forty-acre or so farms spreading over the lowland for half a mile or more from us. Larger farms sloped up over the ridges and hills to meet the timberline. The earliest farmers had scooped out an irrigation ditch along the bottom of the valley and a similar ditch was later dug at a higher level. Water flowed all summer long from the ditches to keep the meadows and pastures green, but the grazing slopes above turned brown in summer.

In Thorp there were sidewalks made of boards with cracks between them, or beaten paths to walk on. Pebbled and sometimes potholed streets carried the horse-and-buggy traffic. The houses and store buildings were sparingly built of local lumber with chimneys of imported bricks. Pail-size boulders from the riverbank, set at intervals of several feet,

kept the underbeams of buildings from touching bare
ground. When I was seven they built a two-story schoolhouse with a furnace and plumbing that replaced the stoves
and privies. However, luxuries like those installed in the
new schoolhouse would not be found in other buildings at
Thorp for many years to come — if ever.

A couple of blocks beyond the depot was Newman's livery
stable. Just beyond it was the millrace which flowed from
the river at a low wooden dam two miles up the valley and
soon widened into a millpond for floating logs. From there
the millrace tumbled down in a milky four-step waterfall
and went rippling over its gravelly bed for two miles to join
the river again.

When the millrace poured down from the millpond
through the penstock and out the water wheel, wheels
whirled upstairs grinding the farmer's wheat into flour for
his family and millfeed and shorts for his horses and cattle.
It turned saws that sliced logs into timbers and boards, then
planed them smooth for building houses, barns and even the
Methodist church with its steepled belfry. At night it spun
a dynamo that sent out electricity to light up houses in the
village and on some farms. On Tuesday and Thursday
mornings it heated the electric irons. Then, best of all, it
paused among the trees and bushes in back of the livery
stable and deepened into a quiet, inviting swimming hole
where we boys could splash and laugh in the clear cool water
or sprawl out lazily on the sunny bank.

When home from the swimming hole I was likely to see
signs of mysterious things going on in the sawdust-carpeted
saloons and whispered-about houses with drawn blinds
crowding us on two sides. I remember watching from our
yard as a few boisterous young women got out of a hack at a
remodeled barn across the street. Pasco Sadie may have been
one of those young women, as I saw that name scrawled on

the wall inside the reconverted barn where, in later years, I often sat on a stool milking our Jersey cow.

My parents were active in church, did not drink, smoke or swear, while I was always trying to show the other kids I was not that good. In our untamed surroundings I could easily find some way to practice not being too good, and I would try to make sure the older boys had no cause to call me a piker when my chance came to follow them into any mischief they might be up to.

Bob Heneby and Frank Dalby were the most fun. Both were usually dressed in too short, blue denim bib overalls and contrasting shirts. Frank liked to wear a black felt hat with turned-up brim, but a short-visored canvas cap was good enough for Bob. Bob's hair and eyes were dark and Frank was blondish, while there I was with long reddish hair and freckles. Neither Bob nor Frank took much to books, and perhaps that influenced me not to either. Bob's dad was the upper ditch walker while Frank's dad was our blacksmith. Bob lived alone with his dad. Frank had both his parents, two sisters and a brother. At first sight Bob and Frank had seemed too wise and tough for me to pal with, but then Bob grinned at me as though he had at last found the brother he wanted. After that he would help me hold my own with Frank, or if necessary with anyone else. Bob was not inclined to big talk the way Frank was and seemed the kinder. But when it came down to it, Frank's big heart showed itself in a way that his outward bluff could not conceal. Both well knew how to swear and my mother would sometimes forbid me playing with them. Then with a guile she could not oppose they would promise not to teach me any more bad words and I would be basking in their company again.

For a small boy who had room for a tender, juicy apple as often as I did, life in Thorp was all the better. The first residents had, with commendable foresight, set out apple trees in their yards, and after a few years of Thorp's existence, hardly a house was without a few. However, there must have been widely-shared disappointment when some of the trees came into bearing and it was found that their fruit, though abundant, was hardly worth picking. Most of the apples were left to fall as hog feed or for boys to use as ammunition in mock battles of war.

In a neighbor's orchard on our alley was a Wolf River apple tree that bore the largest apples I've ever seen. There were enough other kinds of better quality, so little use was made of Wolf Rivers. But they looked so tempting in their pink-red stripes that we boys could not resist swiping one or two apiece, even though we knew one bite would be all we wanted. Smaller, less colorful apples such as Russets and Greenings or maybe Pearmains were safe from us. But anyone owning a Yellow Transparent or June apple tree had better keep an eye on it, if he wanted enough left for pie or sauce.

I could fill up with apples in our own yard, but we only had three varieties as a result of the tree peddler having unloaded several trees of each kind on the original owner. There were more than enough sweet apples, so that along about the first of August others in the village were welcome to pick all they wanted. But they did not come as they probably had sweet apples in their own yards. When ours were barely ripened, though, I would champ my fill of them.

Happily, the tree peddler had endowed our yard before I was born with a few rootstocks bearing the aristocratic name "Duchess of Oldenburg." I never knew how apple trees with a proud name like that ever grew up in the homely, humble precinct of Thorp. I did know that the yellow-green, red-striped apples I found high up on them in early September would make a so-called Delicious apple seem to taste like an uncooked pumpkin. The delicate fragrance and dew-kissed beauty of a barely-ripe "Duchess" truly told of its sweet, yet tart juiciness inside. Nothing ever tasted better to me than the browned apple dumplings in lemoned sauce my mother made with not-quite-ripe Duchess apples picked the same morning. Also in our yard was a tree that bore plenty of mouth-watering apples for wintertime. It was probably a Winesap, but we called it "the winter apple tree."

Our yard had four big cherry trees, but two of them were hardly worth climbing, their fruit was so poor. Then there were five pear trees. Nobody cared for the pears from two of them — that is, nobody except our big dog Major, who was Saint Bernard and mastiff in equal parts. In season he would lie on the grass beneath one tree and gingerly snap at and devour yellow jackets feeding on the pears he had, with shrewd foresight, bitten open for use as bait. Getting stung annoyed but never deterred Major from getting his fill of crisp, juicy yellow jackets.

So we had apple, pear and cherry trees everywhere, but not a sprout of an apricot, plum or peach tree. And since other yards were not much better off than ours, the tree peddler probably never showed his face in Thorp again after it became known just what he'd sold the residents there.

When winter came to Thorp and the temperature went below zero we would have big times skating on the frozen millpond. It had many times the room needed to cut a figure eight on, but I'd never quite learned how by the time the ice melted at the end of winter. It took less skill and gave more thrills to be flung off the tail end of a crack-the-whip, long line of skaters. A good deal of our skating fun was in taking time out to get near the warmth of a crackling bonfire built on shore.

The occurrence each January that made me afterward eager to toast my feet at a red-hot stove was the Sunday afternoon sleigh ride. My father somehow had invested more in a corduroy-upholstered bobsleigh than he had in our only buggy. So for him to get enough return on his larger investment he had to take us for a sleigh ride, usually on the first very cold Sunday afternoon of the year. That would be all, because by the time we got our numbed feet thawed out, the snow would be gone until the next December.

In the dead of winter when the ice was eight or ten inches thick, most of the prospering farmers would come to the millpond with their two-horse bobsleds to haul home a summer's supply of ice. It made a man sweat even in zero-degree weather to saw the ice up into chunks the size of a square doormat. In an icehouse on the farm the blocks were laid about six deep and surrounded with a thickness of sawdust to keep them from melting too fast in summertime.

We had neither an icehouse nor an icebox but did have a sawdust-insulated cellar to refrigerate home-canned and fresh foods. A cool jar of juicy tomatoes brought from the cellar and salted on a hot summer afternoon refreshed my parched palate as nothing else could. For there was no garden like one in Thorp to give tomatoes the clean fresh tang they always kept when canned and stored in our old cellar. Also in there were crocks full of Jersey milk with deep layers of cream on top. It would have been hard to keep the fingers of any small boy out of the crocks, if he liked cool thick cream the way I did.

Even the spring wind was not strong enough to get inside our cellar, but it could in a day almost blow the life out of me. There was a lone walnut tree in front of the blacksmith shop that never grew so much as a twig on the weather side. And you knew there'd be little the wind could still blow down after the first spring gale. A kite strong enough to get up in the Thorp wind would carry you away if you hung onto the string too long. But the same wind made you glad to be lying in the sun behind some board wall out of it. And when snug in bed at night it felt good to hear it flapping or rattling anything that would move. But the best time was a day or a week in May when the sun felt warm and the wind was nowhere in Thorp and nowhere in the green and blooming fields and hills surrounding it.

Fishing in the wind was no fun, but the first windless day in spring gave me the urge to hike off to the millrace with my pole. First I had to get a couple of fishhooks from our store. Royal coachman and brown hackle flies looked good to me and would look good to trout, I thought. I tied my line to the more colorful royal coachman and stuck the brown hackle on my hat brim the way Indians did. Pennywinkles lived in shells on the bottom of the irrigation ditch in front of our house, so I dredged up a few and put them in a tobacco can for bait. I saw tall Burt Grove coming on the sidewalk, then stop near me. He was dressed in blue bib overalls that almost covered his blue checked shirt. The drooping brim of a straw hat shaded his grinning face.

"Now, Chub," he cautioned me, "you oughta leave some a them trout in that millrace for us to catch later on, you know."

"Yeah, I know," I replied to Burt who walked away, laughing to himself.

Ready to catch fish I crossed the street, went past the depot to the livery stable and then to the bank of the millrace. They fished down below the bridge so I went there. At a calm place between riffles where it looked like there should be trout, I stopped and sat on a rock. I liked to listen to the millrace. But the time had come for me to impale a pennywinkle on my hook. It was not the fun I wished fishing would be.

At last I got the royal coachman baited and sunk in the

water. I waited. In a while I felt a tug on the pole and jerked out what looked like a trout. I'd seen much bigger ones. The next on my hook was the same size. It had taken a long time, and I decided that was enough for me. Mama would cook them for dinner.

When I got in front of our store, there came Burt Grove again. He stopped and said:

"Say, Chub, where'd you get them minnows? They ain't even trout minnows. Too bony to eat. Them's nothin but chubs."

"Yeah? They look like trout, though. What're chubs?"

"They're squawfish," Burt rather haughtily informed me. "Squaws eat them is all."

"Well, Mama will cook them for me anyway . . . when she sees them."

As Burt walked away he threw back:

"Go ahead then if you want to grow up to be a squaw."

Mama cooked my fish thinking they were trout, I guess. And I ate them knowing they were chubs.

Chapter 3

EVERYONE KNEW THEM

When the local freight stopped at the Thorp depot on Monday, Wednesday and Friday mornings, Mr. Splawn was waiting for it. The word DRAYMAN, deep-set in a shiny metal plate on the front of his cap, gave him official standing in my eyes. His dray was a light farm wagon whose running gear was painted yellow. Its green box had high sides supporting a seat at the front end. MILBURN painted in big letters on its sides showed it was bought at our store. It did not have sloping top boards like a proud city dray, as I wished it had, but Mr. Splawn lent it personality no dray could acquire in any city.

It was pulled to the depot and backed up to the three-foot-high platform by Prince and Lightning who had worked when young as cattle horses. Little had they dreamed then of being hitched to a village dray wagon and never allowed to run again, or even eat grass. For Mr. Splawn wanted his horses to prance and act hard to handle, and being tied in their stalls and fed plenty of oats when out of harness made them want to run away when pulling the wagon. Side reins tautly anchored to cruppers arched their necks and raised their tails. Breeching and breast straps were also snubbed to help make Prince and Lightning continue to perform like colts the first time in harness. Even after their long and close acquaintance with locomotives, upon the approach of one, Mr. Splawn still made it appear he had to stand at their heads, and while holding their bits calm them with his voice.

Mrs. Splawn ran things at home, but when driving his horses Mr. Splawn had a chance to show who was boss. When not busy with his draying he stayed at home and did the work she wanted done. She was smaller than he was but appeared more stout and stern. Josephine and Helen, her primary grade granddaughters, were in her care. Often she also gave full-time care to other children. Gus Floe left his boys, Arthur, ten, and George, seven, with her so they could attend school. That was some time after their mother had to go to an insane asylum and Gus had to spend most of his time on his timber homestead up Joe Watt Canyon.

It was good news that Gus's wife Effie could return to live up the canyon with him, and the boys could be with them when school let out. Before that, Gus would sometimes come down to Thorp and stay in his two-room house. Then he would usually visit our store after supper. One evening in early spring, Bill Nightingale and a hardware drummer were sitting and visiting near the tall, potbellied, cast-iron stove. My dad was in his chair. Jim Lane waited on a customer near the front of the store. A long wooden box nearly filled with wastepapers reposed beneath my dad's stand-up desk. Nothing was cozier than to sit with my feet dangling down the side of it and listen to Bill and my favorite drummer. It was all the better with the stove roaring as the wind bent and strained the winter-stripped cottonwood out in front. Bracketed on the outside wall above me was a wind-battered, sheet iron Bell Telephone sign. It squeaked and jerked, its rusty nails imitating a frayed string fiddle and bow at a barn dance.

The drummer turned to me and said, "Who's your teacher this year, Chub?"

"Miss Love."

"How do you like her for a teacher?"

"Oh, I wouldn't make him tell that," Bill advised. "Chub

thinks there should be no teachers. But he doesn't want Miss Love to know that."

"Why, what's wrong with Miss Love, Chub?"

"Nothing — I guess. But she makes you read too much and she makes you have to sit with a girl."

"I remember now," the drummer said. "That was her buying a new ruler from Bill today. She looked like you'd have to mind your p's and q's in her room all right. Is that what you mean, Chub?"

"I guess so."

"The worst of it is," Bill said, "she's thinking of taking Chub with her to Tacoma next summer. So a little bird told me."

I thought Bill was only teasing me; but to make sure they knew where I stood, I said, "I wouldn't go with her anyplace I didn't have to." I was glad to see my dad nodding and that he'd probably missed hearing what I'd said.

"Well, Chub, anyway I think you have a good, capable teacher," Bill emphasized. "She is very well thought of, too."

I heard the back side door open and close. It was Gus. To see him shuffling his feet up the aisle toward the stove brought me up to open-mouthed attention. He was a small man with a short sandy mustache. The brim of his hat turned up sharply. The straight short pipe that stuck from his mouth was out. Standing in front of the flickering stove door, he began to unbutton his mackinaw jacket.

"Eh, heh — good evening, yentlemen," Gus said hopefully, now with pipe in hand.

"Good evening, Gus," my dad roused up and answered, as though glad he'd come. "Haven't seen you lately. There's a seat for you."

Gus smiled. "Tanks. Tanks wery much." But Gus would not feel at home in even a broken-down, wicker armrest chair, so he stood an apple box on end beside the coal scuttle, handy to be near when he had to empty his pipe or spit. There was a moment's silence, then Bill spoke:

"When did you come down, Gus?"

"First ting dis morning, hiking all de vay. Eh, heh. So's to fetch Artur and Yeorge some a Dad's biscuits. Eh, heh. Not dem sea biscuits neider."

"How long were you at sea, Gus?" Bill asked.

"Oh, I tink maybe ten, leven years vhat you say before de mast from Norvay."

A repeated jingling of the front doorbell told that the door had been opened and closed. It was Dobie Shaw, for there was the sound of his voice coming down the aisle. Soon I could see Jim Clyburn coming down the far aisle, smiling to himself. My oldest brother Chas followed him. Jim had a small farm and did team work near the village. Dobie had come to live in Thorp after a life of hard work on his Thorp Prairie wheat farm. He was lank and bent from heavy labor when young, as men of his generation commonly were. His long sandy mustache was tobacco-stained. After long years of plowing and reaping wind-swept, sun-baked fields, his blue eyes still squinted.

"What d'yuh think Clyburn done now?" I heard Dobie ask in a hurt tone when near the stove. (Mr. Clyburn looked amused.) "Why, he done let them dogs belongin to me'n Chas scatter out. Ever last one of em." Dobie let himself down into the wicker chair. Mr. Clyburn with legs crossed sat on a nearby nail keg. Chas, smiling, stood near the door into the house. Dobie squirted tobacco juice into a flat box of ashes. "Here me'n Chas nearly done broke our bank payin him for doin nothin but herd em. We had a whole big band a the smoothest dogs you ever seen in Thorp. Dang it all. Chub there would a done better'n him."

"I wonder what you were doing with so many dogs?" the

drummer asked, seemingly taken in by Dobie's feigned
seriousness.

"Why, we was aimin to turn out a whole boxcar full a hot
dogs. Had everything in shape to a done it. Now Clyburn
there done ruined our whole business. Dang it all."

"Well, Dobie," Mr. Clyburn said, "pay me a month's
wages, and I'll round up every last one of your dogs."

"Not on your life," Dobie objected. "You was paid once
to tend em so's they couldn't run off. You'd just go and let
em loose again."

"What'd you say you wanted them for?" the drummer
asked, as though at a loss.

"Why, hot dog sausages. Prime dogs like them would a
made the tastiest sausages you ever eat. A course them dogs
knowin that, soon as they seen Clyburn sleepin on the job,
ever one of em hightailed it clean out a the valley. There
ain't nough left in town now to make up a dogfight." Saying
that started Dobie to laugh and laugh as he bent up and
down, then spat out more tobacco juice. His listeners had to
laugh, too, Mr. Clyburn most of all.

It took Dobie a few moments to recover enough to say,
"Well, Gus, how're things up in Joe Watt? I reckon by now
you done eat up all that sack a sugar you took up there on
your back that winter. It was most as big as you, like Orr
here said."

"Yah," Gus said with a smile as he flexed his arm. "Ye
get muscle like dis from shippin out on, I tink, tirty woyages
in wind-yammers."

"What made you want to ship out, Gus?" Bill asked.

Bill was from London. From there he brought to our
store a tall silk hat immured in a scarred, hard leather case.
It was a leading curiosity in Thorp, even though little worn
except in school theatricals. Before Thorp knew Bill, his
brother Tom had worked in our store. Bill was a drug ad-

dict in London, but Tom thought that life in the fresh air of Thorp would cure him. My parents also must have thought there was a chance of it, since he was given a job in the store and a room in our house when he came. Bill had been a linen expert in a huge London department store, according to Tom, and Bill never denied it. So Thorp was lucky to have a linen expert to unroll the half bolt of linen in its only dry goods store. I was sorry there wasn't enough linen to make it worth his while. It might have helped more than Thorp's bracing climate did to lick his habit.

I knew that Bill, now and then professing illness, would hole up in his room. No one could enter, not even the doctor, unless they broke down the door. It was like a resurrection when at last one day he would open the window enough to entice me over to it. Handing me fifteen cents, he would entreat me to fetch a can of sardines and a box of soda crackers from the grocery store. He knew I'd never delay doing him a favor. The sardines and crackers worked like magic to get Bill back on his feet and into the store waiting on customers again.

When Bill and Carl Dean had to play a trick on our newlywed doctor, they paid my brother Pat and me a dime each to do the dirty work. There was no way we could refuse Bill. In a way we were paid to do what every boy in the village tried to do anyway. That was to find one or more empty medicine bottles and for a nickel each sell them to the doctor who ran the drugstore. Anyway, Bill and Carl supplied us with bottles we could sell to the doctor for a price, in addition to the dime each they paid us. That seemed a good way to get rich. Only to do it we would have to get up at dawn and go wake the doctor to bargain with him. Once at his door, we knocked, then waited until the serious-faced doctor in his nightgown faced us, no doubt fearing my mother was in need.

"Do you want to buy some bottles?"

"No!"

We were glad not to be too near the door as it slammed shut. We scampered in a hurry back to our beds. Bill and Carl may have enjoyed the trick, but Pat and I could see no fun in it.

Bill like Gus was small in size and short in height. Bill was dark. Gus was sandy. Although a peaceable man, Gus probably could have broken Bill in two with one hand. Bill now and then got maudlin over his little boy Tommie and little girl Maggie whom he had left with their mother in London. When Gus's two small boys lost their mother he kept them with him. It was hard work to do that and have to make a living, but he would never let them into the care of anyone but Mrs. Splawn and then only when they had to be put in school. He had since then greviously missed them but soon at the end of the school term would have them back with him to stay.

Bill was the only one living in Thorp who wore a wing collar. Gus was the only one with tattooing on his hands, an anchor with the letters *AF* on one hand and a blue eagle on the other. I gazed at them every chance I got. Bill had a polished London accent. The roughness in Gus's Norwegian accent I imagined came from sailing so long on the ocean. Bill did not want to give up his English citizenship. Gus treasured his American citizenship probably more than any native-born knew how to.

"Only ting I remember vas dat square-rigger layin at Bergen dat day lookin to me like maybe a chance to get away from hard vork. Ye see nobody'd tole me dat's vhat a square-rigger vas built for, too. To giff you hard vork. Eh, heh."

"It wasn't harder'n balin hay, was it, Gus?" Dobie asked curiously.

"I tink so. Ye get done balin hay sometime. Ye don't

never get done holystonin a square-rigger deck. Ye yust keep rubbin dat stone round and round on dem boards and keepin busy doin a tousand oder tings."

"So you signed on the ship, eh, Gus? Where'd it take you to?" Bill asked.

"Vhere'd it take to? First ting to Liverpool. It vas a Britisher, you know, dis time steerin for Cape a Good Hope. Eh, heh. Tasmania vas down dat vay. Also New Zealand, Auckland and dem oder ports I vas in two, maybe tree times, I tink."

"I wonder what you can do on a ship like that, Gus? You don't have any cows to milk," Jim said.

"Oh, I tink pick oakum, splice cables and paint whole ship and tings like scrubbin decks oder times."

Around Thorp no one could splice a broken rope or a cable like Gus could. Such skill often gave him a chance to show he was important to some farmer, more than for stacking hay.

"Dem sails took all kinds of vork, and ye better lay aloft vhen de old man yelled dat. First ting he growled like dis, 'Vhen I tell ye sometin, I don't vant ye to valk, I don't vant ye to run, I vant ye to *fly*, confond ye, *fly!*' " Seated on his apple box by the coal scuttle, Gus could now laugh as he tamped the tobacco in his pipe bowl and then lit it.

"The old man, that's the captain, eh, Gus?" Bill asked.

"Yah, dat's it. De captain a de ship and de king a de ship he is. Besides dat, he's de law and de yudge a ship and sailor out dere on de sea. A ship sailin tru dem terrible storms gotta have tough old man keepin sailors tough, I tink."

"Gus, did you ever sail around the Horn?" the drummer asked. "I'll bet you did."

"Tree times I tink ve vas sailin round dat Horn. Eh, heh. Eh, heh. Down dere is cold vind I tink. You hear bout dat?"

"Yeah, Gus, you read in the paper about it. But there —

you were even in it. It looks like you never went back after the third time."

"Yah, dat's right. Eh heh."

"What does the Horn look like, Gus?"

"I tink maybe like de gate in hell. Maybe vorse. Dem graybeards is vorse dan hell, I tink."

"Graybeards?"

"Yah, dat's dem."

"You don't mean men."

"Naw, vaves big as mountains and vind blowin de sails to treads, makin tunder like cannons boomin aloft."

"What did you hate most going around the Horn, Gus?"

"I vas hating dat hangin on de top yardarm vith my nails in de dark scratchin de ice half de night. Ye tink dat's bad up dere a hundred and fifty feet going dis vay, dat vay? Ye got to furl de sail anyvay. Vhen ye get down on deck ye in vater up to your belly button. Dat's de vay tings ban goin round dat Horn. Vone day dat vind yerkin me off dat ship into de vater. Yust like dat. Albatross, he save me. Dem birds so big dey stretch out twelve foot. I seen it. Dat good ting dis time vhen I'm drownin in vater. Dis vone tinks I'm makin him good meal, but I'm not likin dat. Better I vring his neck. Den he floats and I grab hold a him till dey pull me out a de vater. Odervise I ain't ban here. Eh, heh."

"How'd you get dry, Gus?"

"Get dry? Ye get vet, stay vet. Den ye don't know de difference. It's vorse gettin vet dan stayin vet. Vhen off votch ye keep oilskins on. So vhen ye hear dat invernal 'all hands on deck!' in middle a night, ye ain't gettin up dere half-dressed. You seen dem icebergs? No. Goin round de Horn ve seen em two miles long and high as dat mountain. All over de place dey vere."

"Gus, how long did it take you going round the Horn?"

"Dat last woyage outa Liverpool vos more'n two hundred days till ve seen de Horn. Dose storms banged dat ship bout to pieces. Eh, heh. Ve had to lay back into de Falklands to get a mast and some oder tings."

"Gus," Jim said, "didn't you get shipwrecked one night?"

"Dat's right. Up dere at Von de Fuca. De old man vos steerin by Tatoosh Light back and fort, back and fort, vaiting for vest vind. Den de vind first ting com blowin too hard and dat ship grind up on de beach in de dark. Nobody lost dat time. Yust getting good and vet some more. Ve valk all de vay to Neah Bay vhere dere is Indians giving us tings to eat. Den dey paddle us all de vay to Port Anyeles."

"How'd you get to Thorp, Gus?" Bill asked.

"Oh, vorkin in voods sometimes. Dat business also good and vet, so I come to Torp to get dry. Eh, heh."

Upon arriving in Thorp, Gus found a job on a farm. While there he married Effie, the sister of the farmer's wife. It was afterward rumored that Effie's sister had contrived the marriage. Anyway, Gus and his bride moved up onto their timber homestead. At times they lived in Thorp where I remembered seeing her when I was very small and somehow knew she was not right. One night I heard her screaming on the road in front of their place. That might've been the night they came and took her away to the asylum.

"Say, Gus," Dobie said, "yuh gonna have the American flag up on your pole again, come next Fourth?"

"You bet I am. Dat's helpin elect Teddy Roosewelt, I tink. Eh, heh."

"Last Fourth, it were, we drove up Joe Watt fur a picnic," Dobie said. "When we come to Gus's place back in a clearing among them big pines, there was Old Glory a wavin high up on a pole. An there was Gus and his boys dressed up to celebrate the Fourth. They was even shootin firecrackers. Say, Gus, when I seen your place you had a fair piece about your house cleared a timber. How'd yuh get rid a all them big ol pine stumps?"

"Dat's easy. In de old country dis is de vay dey do it. You yust take a big old auger and bore a hole straight into de stump all de vay. Den ye bore a chimney hole clear down to it from, I tink, twelve inches maybe fourteen up de stump. After dat put some pieces a trash into de bottom hole and light it. Keep it burnin. Don't let it out. Den vhen it ban burnin good inside de stump ye can't put it out. It'll keep burnin under snow down to zero till dere ain't notin left a dat stump. Yust some ashes. Eh, heh."

The talk continued back and forth, making me drowsy. Soon I could hear only the droning of words and slumped over on my bed of wastepapers and went to sleep.

"Come on now, Gordon. You have to get up and go to bed. Just because Mama went out for a while is no excuse for being late. Hurry up."

I opened my eyes and saw there was no one but Papa left I could listen to. So I was glad to go into the house and into bed with the least preparation I could get away with.

Chapter 4

WE INITIATE ELLADINE

Rushing through the house one day on my way into the store, I saw my mother sitting in the parlor with Mrs. Hollenbeck, who'd come to stay with us while my father and mother went to Spokane to see a doctor. Mrs. Hollenbeck was quite fat and had gray hair put perfectly in place atop her head. She was, my mother explained, a cousin of Miss Love my schoolteacher. On hearing that, I could only hope that my teacher and her cousin were not much alike. Later, when I found that Mrs. Hollenbeck required us to stay either in the yard or in the house when not at school, I knew she was too much like her cousin.

It was because of Mrs. Hollenbeck I happened to be wearing my good clothes in the yard with my brothers on Saturday morning as Miss Love and Elladine, whom I sat with in school, came walking on the boardwalk that ran beside our front fence. Miss Love's brimmed straw hat, nearly matching her dark hair, tilted up in back as though propped on the hair she had knotted there. The brim turned up at the sides but sloped down in front. Her dress had a high neck and a full skirt that hardly cleared the ground. It was made of pink-mixed material with white lace around her wrists and on her shoulders. She seemed a little shorter and was more plump than the other teachers at school and tended to have a double chin. But her flashing dark eyes and always neat, dark brown hair drew the most attention. She had hold of Elladine's hand as they walked quickly along. When

they got to our gate and Miss Love opened it I was concerned, even though as they walked to the front door she
nodded and smiled at us. They were soon inside, leaving me
to wonder more than ever what was up.

Pat and Mike discussed the matter with me and we con-
cluded that Miss Love and Elladine had come to visit Mrs.
Hollenbeck. Sure not us, we agreed.

"This is a good chance for us to go over by Tim's to see
them guys playing marbles," I whispered.

"Yeah, but Mrs. Hollenbeck might find out we're gone,"
Mike objected, also in a whisper.

"Aw, come on. We don't have to worry about her. Least
not with Elladine and them in there with her," I argued.

After we made sure no one was spying out the window,
the three of us slithered through a hole where a picket was
missing in the back fence. Then we took off like three blue
streaks and in no time at all arrived safely in the space between Tim's cellar and the lunch counter shack. Frank and
Bill were playing marbles in a bullring marked out a yard
wide in the dirt. Several glassies striped with all colors were
in the center. Bob was watching and I joined him. Bill,
knuckling his red agate taw, picked off a glassie that darted
out of the ring like a shot. Then it was Frank's turn. Mike
and Pat began tossing pebbles up onto the cellar roof and
watching them roll down. It was all fun while it lasted. The
beginning of the end came when Bob said:

"I better go take a look to see if anybody's comin. You
know who I mean, Chub."

"Yeah, see if the coast's clear," I said.

Bob went and peeked around the corner of the cellar,
then came rushing back.

"Hurry up, Chub. You an Pat an Mike better scat back
that way outa here. I seen *you know who* what's stayin with
you a comin out there in front a lookin mad."

On hearing that, I streaked out for our back gate with Pat and Mike not far behind. All out of breath we reached the gate, only to find it securely tied shut. So we had to squeeze back in through the hole in the fence — the same way we had gone out.

"Hurry up!" I urged Pat and Mike. "Let's get up there and be swinging if she comes looking for us."

There being only two swings, Pat and Mike sat in them while I began gently pushing Mike. As time went on, I began to worry that Mrs. Hollenbeck never would come to see how angelic we could be at play. At last I saw her come from in front of the store and whisk through the gate. Apron flying, she came charging around the house, then to a sudden stop upon catching sight of us. With a look of amazement she threw up her hands.

"Where in the world have you rascals been?"

"Right here," I assured her.

"You were not there when I called you."

"Oh. Maybe we were back there laying on those box shooks." That was a good place for us to be, I thought.

"Then why did you not hear me call you?"

"I think we were sleeping that time," I lied.

"Well, it's a good thing I did not catch you out of this yard. And the next time you had better not be sleeping either. Now get into that house and get ready for dinner!"

Inside the house Miss Love and Elladine were setting the table. On seeing us Miss Love said:

"Where were they, Eleanor?"

"Well, if you can believe it, two were sitting in the swings and the other was pushing them as nicely as could be. I am glad they were doing nothing worse. Gordon would not tell me a story, at least not after all you have taught him in school, Myra."

"Yes, I have tried to teach him to be truthful and I am sure he would be truthful with you, Eleanor."

Their talk worries me. I wonder what they mean. If they don't know I could tell a story, I know. And it worries me they'll find out what I know.

"Well, of course, in case of any doubt, I could always get the truth from either Patrick or Michael."

She'd better not ask them. They might blurt out everything before I could get a chance to tell them. Why doesn't she stop talking that way?

"Yes, Eleanor, you could, but Gordon is so truthful, I think you can depend on what he says."

She knows better'n that. I wish they'd say what a liar I am, when they make me be.

"Well, Myra, you know I think no one is more worthy of praise than a little boy who will not deceive you even to conceal his mischief. Remember that story of George Washington and the cherry tree?"

"Oh, of course. He set such a fine example for other little boys."

Yeah, I heard about that. But the whole thing sounds like a lie to me. If I couldn't tell a lie, I'd be in trouble every day.

"Gordon, look at me," Mrs. Hollenbeck said. "You know about George Washington and the cherry tree and how he got to be President by telling the truth about cutting it down?"

"Yes, ma'am, I remember now. We was over by Tim's place. Not very long, though."

"See there, I told you Gordon could not tell a story when he got a chance to think it over. And, Gordon, for telling the truth and not being gone very long, you will not be punished this time. Do you agree, Myra?"

"Well, yes, I think I can agree to that since he did own up in time."

"Then now we can enjoy our dinner together, and afterward Elladine and Gordon may go on an errand for me," Mrs. Hollenbeck promised. She sounded as though she thought I ought to be elated.

After eating our dinner, we sat at the table waiting while Mrs. Hollenbeck and Miss Love talked about their family. At last we had permission to leave the table, but not before Mrs. Hollenbeck said:

"Gordon, Miss Love says Elladine may go with you to Mrs. Beal's. She is not well and I want to send her some of my corn bread. Be very careful with it. You will have to wear your hat. I see Elladine is wearing hers and you must try to look as dressed up as she does."

I hated wearing my Sunday hat any day, and today I knew it'd make me look too much like Elladine. I wished I could kick Miss Love, who as we were ready to leave said:

"See, Eleanor, how much they look alike with their light auburn hair. Both have freckles, too, but you can see he is richer with them than she is. Still, if he had pigtails and a wide-brimmed hat with ribbons in back like hers, we could scarcely tell them apart."

It disgusted me to see how words suggesting such an outrageous getup amused both ladies. While Miss Love was putting the finishing touches on Elladine's hair and adjusting her hat I slipped out the front door and to the front gate. Mrs. Hollenbeck called to me.

"Gordon, you wait right there for Elladine. Let her carry the bread. Walk all the way with her, and as soon as you leave Mrs. Beal's, come straight back home."

"Yes, ma'am," I answered, but not loud enough for her to hear, so I had to repeat it.

Besides her ribbons Elladine wore an all trimmed and

ruffled pinafore of light blue polka dot. Even in my Sunday clothes I shrank from being near her, to say nothing of walking in plain view with her. So it shamed me in one way and elated me in another when, as we turned the corner, I saw Bob, Frank and Joe coming toward us, smiling sympathetically, I thought. They stopped to let us pass. Bob spoke, his eyes twinkling.

"Gosh, Chub, you're lucky havin Elladine come to see yuh. On Saturday, too!"

"You boys had better leave us alone," Elladine warned. "We're taking something good to Mrs. Beal."

"See there, Bob," Frank said in a mock-serious voice. "I always told yuh she wasn't so bad. What yuh takin her, Ellie?"

"Don't you dare call me that. It's not my name and you know it."

"Yeah, but it's better'n your own one," Frank retorted, as he kicked some dandelion blooms.

"So is any other name better than yours, smarty. Come on, Gordon. We have to go."

"Stick around, Chub," Bob urged. "I know somethin we kin do. Elladine too, maybe."

That was probably Elladine's first invitation to join a notorious gang, and she could not resist showing some interest.

"What do you mean?" she asked.

"Don't you know? We got a place down that alley there that's lots of fun."

"I'm not going down that alley. Go by yourselves. Me and Gordon have to go to Mrs. Beal's. Gordon, you know what Mrs. Hollenbeck said. We'll be late. Come on."

As much as I wanted to stay with the boys, Elladine made me think it was better not to. It did not take very long to get to Mrs. Beal's. I stayed out on the road while Elladine went to the front door and politely presented the corn bread. On our way back home she got curious about the alley.

"What fun is there down that alley, Gordon? Have you been down there?"

"Sure, lots of times with Bob and Frank."

"What all do you do?"

"I can't tell you. They won't let me."

"Oh pshaw, Gordon! You can too. They can't hear you tell me."

"Yes they can. They're coming there now. Probably been waiting to tell you, so I don't have to."

Frank was first to greet us. "Now we kin have some fun down the alley, if Ellie — I mean Elladine comes along. Down the alley's the quickest way to Chub's place, Ellie — dang it! I mean — I should a said Elladine, a course."

"Sure, come on!" Bob exclaimed. "We'll take you clear down there. Won't we, Chub?"

"Well — maybe I'll go this time. Don't you kids get me mussed up though. You better not, cause you'll get in trouble with Auntie if you do."

"Naw, Elladine," Bob assured her, "we wouldn't do nothin like that. This is a real intrestin place where we're goin. There ain't nothin as good as it around here. Miss Love'll maybe wish she was there along with us."

"I'll go just this once, but don't you tell her ever. I'm not sposed to go."

Going down the alley Frank walked on one side of Elladine and Bob on the other. Joe and me brought up the rear. I knew we were headed for Wyatt's barn, and in no time at all we came to it.

"Here's the place," Frank announced. "Now, Elladine, you kin follow up to where we're goin. It's where the fun is." He slyly winked at me as Bob and Joe gave me the kind of looks only happy conspirators can ever have.

"Where is it?" Elladine demanded. "Gordon has to come with me, or him and me have to go home. Auntie says you kids are always into some mischief."

"Chub'll go with you, won't you, Chub?" (I nodded to answer Bob's question.) "Me'n Frank'll go first'n get it ready. Joe, you stay here with her and Chub." Frank and Bob disappeared inside the barn. In a moment Frank opened the door enough that he could motion me to come in.

"Wait here a minute, Elladine. They want me to come in and help them. Joe's still here," I assured her.

"I won't wait and you have to come with me or I'll tell on you — everything. . . . Well, then go in, if it's only one minute."

As soon as I was inside, Frank whispered half out loud to me, "Chub, you get her up there. She said she'll go with you. You know how we did you that time. It was just for fun. Remember?"

"Go on and do it, Chub!" Bob urged. "So's we kin die laughin at her. Soon as you and her's up there you kin scat back down the ladder. Time you do that we'll be pullin it down. She'll be so high up she can't get down."

I thought Bob would explode trying to keep from laughing. Frank too. As soon as they could look halfway sober we all went out to where Elladine waited with Joe.

"Gordon! You took more'n a minute. We have to go now."

"No, Elladine, wait a minute," Frank argued. "We was up there gettin it all ready. You know we had to fix up that playhouse up there so you could play house in it."

"Yeah, it's even got chairs and a stove in it," Bob said excitedly. "Why don't you and Chub go up and see it. There wouldn't be no room for everybody. We'll wait out here."

"Hurry up then, Gordon. I'll see if it's the truth. Show me what's up there."

"Elladine, Bob and me don't lie. Hurry up and show her, Chub," Frank urged.

Back inside the barn there was a long ladder going up through a hole into the hayloft where there was no hay. With my encouragement Elladine started slowly up the ladder. I kept close to her feet. In a minute she was on the floor of the loft.

"Where is it?" she demanded.

"Way down that way," I said, pointing.

By the time she had gone ten steps I was down the ladder to the floor where Frank, Bob and Joe waited. They had the ladder lying down on the floor almost as soon as I was off it.

"Let's all get out of here!" Frank commanded.

"Where you goin, Chub?" Bob asked.

"With you guys."

We were out of the barn before Elladine had time to yell at us. Frank led the way back up the alley and farther on into the brush near the railroad. I could not resist following him.

We squatted down in a small clearing from where I could peer through the brush to our house. The others chattered gleefully about the trick we had pulled on Elladine. For me, the time to worry had come. I was thinking I'd better take off for home, when I saw Mrs. Hollenbeck and Miss Love come out the front door to the gate. Miss Love came walking on the sidewalk in our direction. It would've been easy for her to cross the street and find us, so I sighed with relief to see her keep on the course Elladine and I had taken to Beal's. After going a few blocks she disappeared around the corner, unaware she could have turned into the alley and found Elladine. In a way I wished she had, but the others seemed tickled to see her miss the chance. I didn't know what else to do but wait. Going home without Elladine seemed out of the question. Then I spied Mrs. Hollenbeck — more awesome than ever — flying out our gate onto the sidewalk with Pat and Mike trotting behind her. They came on rapidly and soon were hurrying on toward Beal's. It looked like it was time for me to get home, so I said a hasty good-bye and took off.

Back in the yard I planned to act as though nothing had happened when Mrs. Hollenbeck and Miss Love discovered me. The problem of Elladine was too much for me to solve, so I dropped it. But it got to be a long wait. Mrs. Hollenbeck had often told us how she'd spank boys who didn't mind her and now I had time to hope and pray she hadn't meant it. Then I heard crying from the alley and soon saw Mr. Wyatt bringing Elladine through the back gate ahold of her hand. She looked like she had been through the mill. Her hat and one hair ribbon were missing. Her face was splotched with dust, and cobwebs clung to her dress, its ruffled hem now torn.

"Gordon, you mean kid!" she half screamed. "Just wait till I tell Auntie."

"Where are your folks?" Mr. Wyatt demanded.

"They went up that way," I said.

"Then let's go find them. I hope they give you what you've got coming."

"Yes, sir," I agreed.

Mr. Wyatt still holding Elladine's hand led the way. I followed. When we came to the turn near the school I could see Mrs. Hollenbeck and Miss Love far beyond Beal's, going toward the mills as though hoping to find us there. It looked pretty bad for me and I felt as low as I could feel. Then I saw Frank, Bob and Joe walking toward the blacksmith shop. They turned and waved cheerily at me. That was one time when I wanted to give each of them a kick.

"Well," Mr. Wyatt said, "I guess we'd better go back to your place and wait for them. They'll have to give up and come home before long."

"Yes, *you*, Gordon! I'm going to tell what you did and I hope you get what's coming to you."

There was nothing for me to say. I was glad to get into our yard and stay there for once. But after a long time I saw Mrs. Hollenbeck and Miss Love come through the gate and go into the house and so I knew the free time I had left in the yard was short. Elladine was in the house. It was Mrs. Hollenbeck who called me in. I saw that two of the rocking chairs in the parlor were in use.

"Myra," Mrs. Hollenbeck sighed, "this is more than I counted on. I don't know what I can do with him. I wish now his parents were here." (That was as good as anything I hoped to hear.) "I don't feel I am the one to take care of him for this."

"Eleanor, I could take him home with me. I do have him in school, you know."

That prospect was the worst of any I could imagine. Anything but that. What she wouldn't do to me for playing a trick on her pet.

"That would suit me just right, Myra."

Oh, now I'm in it. How can I get out of going with her? I wish I'd never seen them kids. They can even laugh now.

"But I promised his parents I would keep the boys and I shall do it. I expect them home Monday, and I will make sure they know about the problem he has given us today."

Yeah. Anyway I don't have to go with Miss Love. What a relief! Maybe by the time Papa and Mama get back they'll feel so good that what I did won't be important to them.

Chapter 5

INDIAN FRIENDS

The wind waved and bent the tall grass growing over the graves of Kittitas Indians buried before 1905 on a lonesome knoll in sight of the upper Yakima River. One was buried when only nine and one when he was ninety. Their ground was about a mile beyond a wooden dam built by Thorp pioneers to boost the millrace out of the river. Going that way one day, Frank and Bob and I crawled through barbed wire fences and tramped for two miles over hot rocks, through sagebrush and thistles, when suddenly four grave-stones appeared. They were two or four feet high, seeming with life, but keeping still and silent inside a hoary picket fence. When Frank whispered that there were spirits inside the fence with the stones, we believed him and took off in a hurry. Long afterward, I went back and saw that some ghoul had dug up two graves, but still clearly engraved on the stones were the following names, dates and ages:

Major Tachnunam, September 5, 1889
Garthlam Pahoster, June 20, 1891, 9 years
Mathalme Pahoster, July 1, 1895
Frank Wyneco, May 15, 1900
Joe Louis, October 10, 1900
Edward Pahoster, April 25, 1903
George Swowtuck, December 7, 1903, 90 years
Samson Swowtuck, December 15, 1904, 30 years

Two unmarked wooden crosses had fallen over, but I knew more than two unnamed on the stones had been buried

Ruth Newman Potter, who was born and raised
in Thorp, sculptured the busts of Antwine
and Lucy from which these portraits were painted.

there. One was Andrew Heenan's mother, who died during the time he and I sat near each other in the second grade. Sometimes the Indian people bought full bolts of cloth at our store to shroud a body for burial. The graveyard was on the property of Lavina Wyneco, buried there near her husband Frank who had died fifteen years before her. No doubt Lavina had caused his name to be engraved on the stone, but no one had done the same for her near the place where she was born so many years before our village of Thorp began.

In keeping with the Indian custom of her day, Lavina wore a bright, red-fringed blanket, her head swathed in an even brighter silk kerchief. Her gray hair showed at the edge of it. On her feet she wore buckskin moccasins decorated with assorted colored beads. Lavina bore herself with dignity. She would not demean herself with the white man's alcohol, and she scorned those of her race who did. But in the long run she could not — nor could her daughter Maggie before her — escape his disease, consumption. And so before it might have been, they were buried there inside the little fence, their names and ages soon to disappear beside the swift river that had nourished them.

On a winter morning when the door from the store into our dining room slowly opened without a knock, it would likely be Lavina coming to visit my mother. Smiling, Lavina would nod and go straight to the cheery, red-hot stove. Sometimes she had walked in moccasins four miles through snow in below-zero weather. My mother would cheerfully greet her:

"Good morning, Lavina."

Lavina spoke her native tongue and some English, but only the earliest white settlers knew many Indian words or the Chinook jargon. Perhaps following the example of the white invaders addressing her, Lavina usually called anyone she knew by their plain last name. My mother didn't mind being called "Orr" by Lavina.

Knowing what Lavina liked, my mother would soon have on the table a plate of fried brown eggs with lean bacon-back and homemade bread, thickly spread with dairy and prune butters. Lavina, then more hungry than cold, would move to a chair near her breakfast. I imagined the smell of fried bacon teased her appetite as much as it did mine. And always enthralled by her presence anyway, I watched hungrily as she feasted upon the eggs and bacon with an audible relish so infectious I could taste every bit. With each bite she smacked and slurped to her heart's content, and I knew how happy my mother was to see the joy her Plymouth Rock eggs with bacon and homemade bread brought to good Lavina on a cold winter morning.

My mother told of the time she overheard Lavina in the store berating John Newman, the livery stable owner. It went like this:

"Newman, me need wood. You bring team come haul em?"

"Oh, Lavina, I wish I could haul you some wood but I been so doggone busy butchering hogs and picking fruit and getting things done for winter, I don't have time. You'll get it in some way, Lavina."

"You no have time! Lavina have time wash baby dities. Scrub. Wife sick. Me come help. Uh! Lavina cold. Newman no have time bring em wood. Me no come more. No have time! Uh!"

"Oh well, all right, Lavina. I owe it to you. Have Masterson get your wood ready. I'll bring a team and haul it next week."

Lavina's daughter, Maggie, went away to boarding school and sometimes Lavina complained to my mother of the treatment Maggie got at school, where she would be homesick and hungering for her native food. Then, one year after Maggie came home from school, she died of consumption.

With my reddish hair and freckles I was no favorite of Lavina's, as my youngest brother was with his black hair and eyes like my mother's. Lavina would tell him she found him a long time ago wrapped in a warm blanket in a hollow stump deep in the woods and brought him to my mother, but now she wanted him back. One day she came to my mother angry because she thought someone had made my brother fear she would hurt him.

Masterson (Matt) Pahoster was the grandson of Lavina. The names of his father, mother and brother appeared on those gravestones long before he was grown. But somehow he lived on, the only survivor of his family, and became celebrated around Thorp for his athletic and riverboating prowess. It was a show seeing Matt in the pitcher's box at Sunday afternoon baseball down across the millrace in the white clover-carpeted clearing. His dark eyes gleamed intensely as he wound up and fired the ball with all his supple might to the catcher crouched in front of the pine stump backstop. He had to look to first base smiling when the batter struck at thin air. The day the two-span railroad bridge fell in the raging, flooding river, they sent for Matt. There was no one else anywhere near Thorp who could pole a skiff taking a line across the swollen torrent.

One time Matt and his Aunt Maggie came to our front door to give my mother pictures of themselves that were in a star-shaped frame. In between the star's points Maggie had woven pink and blue lustre thread.

On a quiet sunny morning Frank told Bob and me that a jail was being built in back of Wade's store, three blocks from the depot. We could hear the carpenters hammering, so we wasted no time in running over to them, wondering

what a jail would look like. We came to a brand new structure smaller than our schoolroom, still without a roof. Two
men were persistently hammering. The outside walls and
inside partitions were built with two-by-fours laid flatwise
atop each other, forming four rooms. One room was equal
in size to the three others. Two small window holes and one
door hole appeared in one outside wall. The other outside
walls were solid to the top. I looked curiously at them for a
while and then shrank back from the carpenter's insinuat-
ingly warm invitation to step inside of what I knew was
being built to keep people locked up.

The quantity of intoxicants daily dispensed by five saloons in Thorp had made it seem necessary to build a jail.
One of its most unwilling tenants was to be Charlie Samson
from across the river. Indian Charlie, as he was called, took
every chance damnably offered him to liven up with fire-
water and exercise his Indian war cries up and down Railroad Street. That usually meant the marshal would have to
compel Charlie, for his own good, to spend a night secured
within the solid walls of two-by-fours.

On one such night a friend of Charlie's paddled across
the river in his dugout, stole a mile to the jail and unbolted
the door hasp. When morning came Charlie was gone. The
news of his escape made quite a stir in the village. I hurried
to the scene, wanting to see what a broken jail looked like.
The unbolted hasp, its padlock still shut, looked weak as a
dishrag hanging on the wall, and the whole jail appeared
much less forbidding with its door swung wide open. That
was all. I heard them say it was jailbreaking and called
for another arrest, but it seemed the marshal was content
to let Charlie stay across the river. As for me, I was sorry
I wouldn't get to hear, at bedtime, any more of Indian
Charlie's war cries until he might think it safe to visit
Thorp again.

Most of the dozen or so Indians who traded in Thorp lived on narrow pieces of land between the bluff and the river. Like Charlie Samson's friend they crossed the river in dugouts. Antwine and Lucy had their forty acres with a cabin on our side of the river. Neither one had grown very tall. No white person knew how old they were, so it would sometimes be told, as though to reveal a secret, what a great age they really were. Anyone could see they minded their business and were content with each other's company.

Lucy came to Thorp wearing the typical shawl or blanket and kerchief, not as brightly-colored as most Indian women wore. Antwine wore a stiff-brimmed felt hat with a couple of trout flies stuck in it and a strap under his chin that tended to give him a somewhat pugnacious look. Perhaps the chin strap was meant to hold his hat on in the wind, but it probably also helped to keep some curious people at the right distance.

It was told that when young, Antwine with other Indians fought the whites who came to possess their valley. The lost battle seemed to have left a trace of resigned bitterness on his countenance, such as it probably left on others who fought in vain with him.

From the road it appeared that Antwine and Lucy had a Yakima teepee set up in front of their unpainted cabin among the trees. I imagined they slept in their teepee in the summertime, but was never bold enough to ask.

In the winter Antwine caught glistening whitefish in the river not far from his door and sometimes had a surplus he would sell in Thorp. I was always glad to see some on our table at dinnertime.

In our store Antwine often wanted to buy "pishhooks." Lucy, unable to make herself much understood, would smile as she pointed at the goods on the shelf, which she wanted to see. One time they came to the store and paid with cash for a heavy, shiny black buggy with two seats. Antwine took the back seat off, leaving a flat box large enough to hold their trappings when they drove up into the mountains to pick huckleberries. Antwine would sometimes bring Lucy to the depot and wait several hours until her train came in. The next day he would be at the depot waiting all day for her. Getting off the train Lucy would be smiling, but I don't remember ever seeing Antwine smile.

Madeline, a young Indian woman, lived up the road a few miles from us, perhaps with Antwine and Lucy. She made a colorful sight in Thorp, riding her big sorrel down the middle of the street, her large beaded bag swinging from the saddle horn. In her hand she held a heavy quirt. Over her black hair was a brightly-colored silk kerchief, and the brightest of blankets covered the rest of her and the stirrups, too. She didn't smile, and her piercing black eyes missed nothing.

One day several of us boys stood along the board sidewalk next to Tim's Place as Madeline rode her horse, clattering down the middle of the pebbled street. It was fun to tease anyone who easily got mad and so when Frank prompted me I parroted his words as loudly as I could:

> *Siwash! Siwash!*
> *That ain't no josh.*

Madeline jerked her horse to a stop and wheeled toward us, snapping her heavy quirt. But we slithered through a fence along the walk where she could not follow on her horse. Mr. Newman with a shovel on his shoulder came walking by and in a sympathetic voice asked her:

"What's the matter, Madeline?"

"Dem son em wahpoos boys alla time yell em 'Siwash! Siwash!' "

Madeline's black eyes flashed angrily. I was thankful that she wasn't able to get near me with her quirt, as we boys took off to get at a safe distance from her.

Our tormenting of Madeline reflected a common attitude of whites toward reds in Thorp, although many were ashamed of it. In my copy of Longfellow's *Evangeline* someone thinking to be funny wrote: "Gordon Orr kissed Susan Abe." She was a poor, lonely little Indian girl who so often looked bewildered in her seat at school.

Chapter 6

SADNESS AND JOY

There was so little room for death in Thorp that when it came it touched all who lived there. In Platt's front bedroom next door to us, when only five, I was shown the lifeless form of Mary, who had lived only long enough to walk a few steps. About a year afterward, George Ames died. He was my age and had lived only a few doors from us in the hotel of half a dozen rooms run by his parents. In their front room I stood beside my mother and looked, unable to understand, at his pale face and at his mother's tear-stained face. Again the white hearse for children, drawn by two white ponies, came out from Ellensburg and led a procession to the silent, marble cemetery on the hill near Patton's grove.

When I was eight Bob still had no brother or sister; then, smiling all over one day, he told us that the doctor would bring him a little brother or maybe even a little sister. Soon afterward, one morning he and I were climbing up and down a boxcar across the road from his house, when with one foot on the bottom rung he turned and said:

"There's Doc Taylor comin now. What d'yuh think's in that black leather bag, Chub?"

"I dunno. You think maybe your baby? It's not big enough for one, is it?"

"A course. Why not? Babies ain't very big at all at first. See, he's goin right into our house now. I bet he's got it."

There was nothing more I could say and Bob thought we'd better go tell Frank so he'd know. But on hearing the news, Frank shook his head as though in doubt the doctor had a baby in his bag. To prove he was right Frank said he would go with Bob and me and wait across the road in front of Bob's house.

After we waited a long while, the front door opened and the doctor came out. He carried his bag just as before, but walked slower, gazing at the ground, shaking his head. It was plain there was something wrong. Neither Bob nor Frank nor I could speak as we watched the doctor going toward his office. We looked back to Bob's house and saw his dad coming toward the gate with his head bowed. When close to us he bent over to kiss Bob and put his arm around him. Then in a husky, faltering voice he told us.

After that, the fear of losing my own mother was all the worse in knowing Bob's mother had not been sick so much as mine had been. It hurt me to see Bob looking so sad. He did not join Frank and me anymore but stayed with his dad. People came to his house. Then finally Mama said we boys should get on our Sunday clothes and go with Papa and her to the service for Bob's mother at our church. As we started out, I saw that the black, rubber-tired hearse and black horses were in front of Bob's house. The sun was dimmed. At other times I had seen Bob walking with his mother to church on the board sidewalk that we walked on. Now Bob would have only his dad to go with him.

Inside the church the doors were folded back so that all the people seated on chairs in the classroom could see the service. Only at such a time did many of them come to church. One glimpse of the gray coffin coming through the green, felt-covered double doors made me lower my eyes to the floor. When I looked up I saw Bob alone with his dad on the front bench. After the minister had prayed a good deal and spoken reverently of Bob's mother, and the songs "We Shall Meet" and "Nearer My God to Thee" were sung, we filed around the coffin and on out into the fresh air. The bell did not swing and ring, but tolled twenty-nine times, my mother said. Two men dressed in black put on tall hard hats and got into the front seat of the hearse. It moved slowly from the church followed by a long line of buggies and surreys.

That was in late February when the fields and yards were still under blankets of snow — too thick for the chinook wind in one day to melt into the ground. But the hoof- and wheel-beaten snow on the roads — not hard enough to resist the gentle warm wind — had turned into slush and soon would mix with the dirt to become mud. Happily, the mud dried out and packed down hard in time for the birth of Kellicuts' baby girl. After going to see her early one morning soon after she was born, my mother sang more merrily than ever at her work in the kitchen.

Then it was Easter Sunday with no wind in Thorp, a perfect day for the birth of spring. In our yard the apple and pear trees were partly in swelling bud and partly in perfumed bloom. Bees were out of their hives contentedly buzzing and flitting from one bloom to another, stopping at each only long enough for a drink of sweetest nectar. Mama said it was time to go look at Specklie, the little hen, who in her first spring had hidden away her nest on the ground under the porch step and laid sixteen eggs in it. We peeked under the step and saw her sitting on the nest and were tickled to see three fluffy little chicks cheeping for her to get up and find them something to eat. Mama lifted Specklie enough for us to see other chicks nearly out of their broken shells. Some had only pecked small holes in theirs. Mama said it looked like all would soon be out pestering their mother to scratch up bugs and worms for them. It was hard to leave them long enough to go inside for breakfast, but we didn't want to miss our colored Easter eggs either.

When we left for Sunday school Mama thought Specklie might have her chicks all hatched out by the time we were back. I begged to stay and see, but remembering that Easter was one day it paid to be at Sunday school helped to get me off to the church.

We were passing Briggs's old barn near the school on our way to the church when something inside the board fence attracted us. We stepped over to the boards and looked between them. Briggs's black cow was on the ground, her side heaving. Near her tail appeared a massive, filmy, balloon-like form that I couldn't make out. I couldn't imagine what was wrong with her, but it seemed to have something to do with Easter. Mr. Briggs came out of the barn and said we made Daisy nervous, to get on to Sunday school. That was what we wanted to do anyway.

In Sunday school Mr. Hornpole, with a pointer, explained to us a big colored picture of the angel standing by a tall stone near the tomb entrance. After that we sang a hymn and then were each given a colored Easter egg. Hopes of seeing Specklie's chicks made us eager to get home, but on our way we saw Daisy standing up and went close to the fence to get a better look. A black and white calf was sprawled on the ground. With her long, rough tongue Daisy dried and smoothed the calf's hair, then proceeded to nudge and lift it behind, urging it to stand. When the calf tried to stand, its legs got all tangled up. But it kept trying until it stood uncertainly on its tall legs and wobbled around to where it could reach and soon half swallow a milk-oozing teat.

We did not want to miss the new calf for one minute, but thoughts of seeing Specklie's chicks out in the sunshine won over the Easter day attraction at Briggs's barn. It only took a few minutes to get home and see that Specklie was up and out scratching in the soft dirt with a clucking that her brand-new, cheeping, gray brood — sixteen of them — already seemed to understand.

So life came to Thorp and it helped to heal the wounds of death. And though each year the cemetery reared more tombstones, life in the village went on as before.

Chapter 7

LOGS DOWN THE RIVER

Pine and fir sawlogs were hauled in the summer and fall on heavy logging wagons and in the winter on bobsleds to the top of a steep bank twenty miles up the river from Thorp. When spring came and the river was near to overflowing, thousands of them were piled there, ready for the six-week "drive" seventy miles downstream to the sawmill. A few hundred feet upstream two wanigans were tied to trees. They had come on a railroad flatcar from the mill, where they'd been stored since the previous spring. Each wanigan resembled a floating, flat-roofed shack about ten by twenty feet in size. One contained a huge cast-iron cookstove with other equipment needed in a kitchen. At the back end were narrow bunks for the cook or "cookee" and the bull cook or "camp louse," and a wider one for the river boss. In the second wanigan were bunks for the "river hogs" — twelve log rollers, and six "breaking" teamsters. A teamster riding one of his two-horse team drove them into the river, hooked onto a log to "break" it loose, then dragged it until it floated in the water. Near the wanigans were three narrow, flat-bottomed riverboats, tapering toward the ends, called bateaux. Laid inside each of them were two iron-tipped, twenty-foot pike poles.

The proud river crew was there, eager to "drive." They were the hardiest, most catlike and daring of the woods crew. Instead of their winter low rubbers they now wore ten-inch-high leather boots with sharp steel calks screwed into the thick soles. Calks would be needed to keep their footing when riding a spinning log through the river's white water. Their heavy woolen pants were stagged and frayed at the bottom. On the drive their wool underwear had to be at least an eighth of an inch thick. Instead of the saw or axe they plied in the woods, a long, heavy-handled peavey with a sharp iron point and hinged hook on the side for rolling logs was now most needed.

At the landing the river boss grasped a heavy sledge-hammer. With it he would knock the wedge from between the bottom front log and the roller leading to the very edge of the bank — twenty feet above the swelling river. A river hog also had a sledge he swung to loosen the wedge at the other end of the log. By some mystic coordination the wedges at each end tumbled over as one, just as the two men dropped their hammers and leaped clear of the logs suddenly come alive. The logs rolled and rumbled and thudded and bounced before hitting the water with a splash that spurted as high as the bank. Now was the select river crew's challenge. Some to the wanigans, some to the bateaux, some to mount their horses, while the river hogs on foot, their peavies at the ready, went tromping down the river's bank.

The water was not far from the melting snow and the river hogs would have to get in it up to their armpits many times. Or a log they had to tread might suddenly shoot out into midstream. Unless the boatmen quickly got the rider off he might fall in over his head. Then it took all the skill of two stout men who had poled bateaux many years on the river to save him from drowning. But when too many logs were running and milling in the current, even the boatmen could not save him.

Every so far logs would get hung up and start a jam that might reach hundreds of feet back up the river. Someone had to go into the center nest and one by one find the key log. When it was found and dislodged it let loose acres of logs — so he'd better get out in a hurry. Sometimes he'd find enough footing on the churning logs to get to shore. Or he might be lucky enough to have a bateau poled his way and not have to ride a spinning log downstream until it touched shore or he plunged into the icy water. It was no wonder the river hogs looked on the bark eaters at the sawmill or on the timber beasts still back in the woods as softies.

The wanigans followed close behind the river hogs and tied up to be near them at mealtime. When the cook blew his horn, usually four times a day to "come and get it," he had better have plenty to get. River men had appetites that were hard to dull, and they thought the world owed them all they could eat. It was hard for any one cook to bake enough pies and cookies the size of plates for one crew always in a hurry. They had to hurry. For just as it takes sunshine to make hay, so it took water to make a log drive. And there was no way to tell how long there would be enough of it to float the wanigans and logs. It depended on how much snow there was and how fast it melted in the mountains. So the drive downriver was always in a hurry to make sure as much as fifteen million feet of logs did not get stuck too high on gravel bars.

One April evening after school as Frank, Bob and I walked up the railroad track we heard the river's roar echoing off the bluff that rose high beside it. Bob said:

"Hear that? The river sounds that way when it gets high. Listen to that kind a *boom!* It's comin from logs bumpin into somethin. Like as though hittin another big log."

"Yeah, sounds like it," Frank agreed. "Boy, that means the log drive is comin! I betcha we'll get outa school early when it's here."

"I sure hope so," Bob said. "I can't wait to eat those kind of cookies and doughnuts they give yuh."

"Me neither," I chimed in with Frank. "Pie, too."

Not long after that, when coming home from school at noon, I saw two men — strangers to me — going in the store door. They wore high leather boots with calks that left dozens of deep marks in the porch planks. Only loggers did that. Curious for more of a look at them, I went into the store in as casual a manner as I could put on. I saw they wanted to buy tobacco and that their pants were wet clear above their knees. So they had to be log drivers. When I saw them go out and cross the railroad and soon disappear through Newman's gate, I knew the log drive boats must be there in back. After that I could not wait and hurried to school expecting that it would let out early for the log drive.

At recess time Miss Love stood facing us as usual. Then, not as usual, she said:

"Children, the log drive is camped in back of Newman's grove today. We have an invitation from Mr. Cross, the foreman, to visit it. So school will be dismissed for the rest of the day, and I shall accompany you down to the river. We want everyone to enjoy it. But there will be dangers there, and since I shall be responsible for you, I want you to mind — the same as you do in school."

In the hall we lined up in our seating order. Then we marched out on our way to the river with Miss Love in the lead. That did not dampen our anticipation, for we were sure there would be plenty we could do when out of her sight on such a rare spring day. Just to see real boats on the river would mean the most excitement since the Fourth of July.

As we walked in line on the narrow soft road through the trees and bushes, we began to hear the familiar noise of the rapids. Then there appeared, as out of a picture book, the

fabulous two wanigans not many steps away. No other boats anywhere near their size ever came down the river. Tied to the nearest one was what looked like a red, double-prowed rowboat. But it had no oars in it. There was a long pike pole protruding from it, though. It looked maybe like an ocean boat and I could hardly believe its being on our river.

A plank, laid from the riverbank to the end of the wanigan, interested me. We boys in a minute would have been up the plank and circling round the biggest stove I'd ever seen. But Miss Love put a halt to that, with a warning that the plank was "too dangerous." Our disappointment soon vanished when a man wearing sort of a white apron appeared and walked down the plank and let the word out that we could help ourselves more or less to the cookies and doughnuts, whose tantalizing fragrance had now begun to affect us. There were heaps of them in bowls on a long table. Miss Love thought it best that each of us take only one cookie and one doughnut. "Leave some for the other pupils now coming in sight," she urged. At least I did not get sick on them, but was ready for more when Miss Love told me I could get in the boat if I wanted a ride across the river.

One pointed end of the boat was nudging the riverbank. At the water end stood a man wearing a wide-brimmed, black felt hat. His light-brown mustache was long and heavy. There were shiny brass buckles on his wide red suspenders buttoned to his pants and stretched up over his shoulders, partly covering his heavy gray wool shirt. With one hand he held a pike pole whose iron-tipped end stood on the gravelly river bottom. When both my feet were in the boat and there seemed to be nothing solid beneath, I realized how secure the ground had been. All was fluid, and there was a scary rocking. But I picked my way through the others to a seat right in front of the man with the pike pole. There it stood close beside me. Behind me I could see a

heavy leather boot and caught a glimpse of the calks, brist-
ling like sharp nail points on the bottom of it.

When the boat was filled with kids, it began to move
away from the land. The other end of the boat pointed upstream. Looking down I could see through clear water to the
gravelly and rocky bottom. The pike pole lifted a few feet,
and when it plunged down I could hear it crunch into the
gravel. The boat lurched ahead. Then on the next power
drive it turned out into the current. I was struck with wonder to see that one man with only a pike pole could keep the
whole boatload of us from upsetting or getting swept down
the river. I hoped it didn't seem that way to him. Wanting
to see how he steered the boat, I worked myself halfway
round.

The rocks on the bottom looked farther down and less of
the pike pole stood up out of the water. Under the water I
could see the pole bend when the man put his strength and
his weight to it. Then I could feel the boat almost shoot out
from under me. I was scared it was caught in the current instead of going to shore, where I was beginning to wish I had
stayed. I glanced up expecting to see the man with the pike
pole looking concerned, but his countenance showed he had
no fear of anything on that river. He just socked the iron
end of the pole down into the gravel, leaned on it and the
whole boatload of kids swung out of the current and, like it
had a lead rope tied to it, glided up the shore. After that, I
was not afraid to cross the river in a boat poled by the man
who stood behind me. And for a few minutes I was able to
enjoy exploring the shore of the river that had always been
for us to only wonder about. It was no different, though,
than the one on our side.

Back at the wanigan each of us got to eat a piece of
prune pie. Miss Love told the cook how fortunate the crew
was to have a baker like him and how happy he had made us.

She then thanked the man with the pike pole, and we got on our way home. But we had hardly seen a single log or a logger with peavey, or the river horses. They were down at the logjam where we could not go because of danger.

Going home we did not have to get back in formation. So, with Frank and Bob I brought up the rear. Miss Love kept looking back at us, but by the time she got to the mill-race bridge it looked like we were safely on our way home. It was very seldom she ever made a mistake like that, so it was probably the prune pie to blame for such a rare lapse in her surveillance.

Someone had closed the gate at the bridge on us. Before we could climb over it, I heard Frank say:

"Hey, you guys. Listen to the millrace! There's a raft down there a ways. Those big kids made it. Let's go and ride down to the logjam on it. That's where the fun is. Are you game?"

"Sure thing!" Bob exclaimed. "How far is it? Come on, Chub! You can go, too. Your folks won't care."

"Yeah, I know they won't," I said, trying to sound confident.

Away we ran down the millrace bank with Frank in the lead. After several minutes he turned and ducked through a bower to the millrace with Bob and me close on his tail.

"There it is," Frank said boastfully. "It's made from some railroad ties. You couldn't sink it no way."

"Fine and dandy," Bob said. "It's big enough for all three of us. Let me untie it. Jump on, Chub."

A pole made from a small willow tree was lying on the bank. Frank picked it up, gave the raft a shove and jumped on with Bob and me. We went floating down the millrace. It was even more fun than the river boat had been. Plunging his willow, Frank tried to imitate the river man with his pike pole. In trying that once too often, he slipped and nearly fell off the raft, losing the pole. It floated away out of reach, and there we were in the millrace current without a rudder.

Bob said, "This thing is going awful fast! That river ain't far from here, either. I can even see the railroad bridge."

"Aw, this ain't nothin," Frank assured us. "We can easy wade to shore from here."

"Maybe *you* can," Bob complained.

"Wait!" Frank exclaimed. "It looks like it might be that logjam ahead there!"

"It couldn't be nothin else!" Bob shouted. "And this thing is goin a mile a minute straight at it!"

"Grab ahold a somethin!" Frank yelled, motioning to me. I shoved my fingers into a crack to help stay on the raft, and after that nobody said anything.

I was too scared to open my mouth, and there wasn't time for it anyway. For not far away from us — tumbled and heaped like jackstraws — were what looked like a thousand logs that I thought the raft was headed like sixty — straight at. Then I saw the river right in front of us, racing like mad through a narrow channel alongside the logs. If we ever got into the current and were thrown against the logs we were goners for sure.

The raft shot out into the fierce torrent and barely missed hitting the logjam as it pitched and plunged downstream. There was an awful rumbling and groaning, and the logs began to move. The crushing and battering sounded louder as every log, it seemed, tried to bump some other one out of the way. The current had us headed straight out in front of the logs. A big one sideswiped our raft, tipping it so I nearly slid off. I gave up for lost when I saw that even Bob and Frank were scared stiff. They had their fingers shoved in the crack too. I was scared that even though we escaped the logs, we'd tumble over the dam onto the rocks below. Suddenly we shot to shore, but before there was time to cheer we hit a boulder and bounced back into the current, all bunched up with the tumbling logs again. Hope had come and gone in a flash. But then I heard a welcome sound. For as when riding in the red river boat, it sounded like a pike pole crunching into the gravel. Then another and another and another crunch. They came louder and oftener and always more welcome. At last, I dared to raise my head to look behind and there it was, red as ever, with river men bearing down on a pole at each end of it. Their determined, weathered faces looked the friendliest I'd ever seen. And as I clung by my nails to the slippery raft, their boat looked safe and snug as a down-lined baby's cradle. Then, just as it got near enough and I was ready to cry with happiness, a log bobbed up between us. But no log could stop such river men for long. And when I looked again, there was their red boat next to our raft. When I heard the command "Hurry up and get in here!" I let go my hold and crawled to and up over the side of the boat ahead of Bob and Frank. By that time I could hear logs and water spilling over the dam close enough to make me shudder. So I was over-joyed to see how calm and unconcerned the river men were as they stood and leaned with all their strength on the pike poles, as the boat glided straight across the current to shore.

Chapter 8

EFFIE

It was spring vacation, so I didn't have to rush off to school right after breakfast but would have a chance to listen to Bill in case he was not busy with a customer in the store. I'd go see. There was Jim, sweeping round the stove as usual. My dad was up in front talking with Mr. Newman and Bill was in back by the bolt rack. He'd wonder why I hadn't gone to school. I sneaked back there so he wouldn't know I was coming. Then I yelled, "Boo!"

"Oh! You Chub! Quit that plaguing me so fresh in the morning. No school today, eh?"

"It's our spring vacation."

"Well, ain't you lucky. It gives you a bit of time to play a few tricks on your old friend Mac, don't it?"

"Yeah, but I don't feel like it."

"Now, bless you, that oughter cheer him up some. What do you feel like?" Bill wore a stiff-billed checkered cap. He got done poking bolts into the pigeonholes and took off his white canvas gloves with the red knit wrists and stuck them under his elbow. Then from his breast pocket he lifted a small, square, shiny box. When its lid popped open Bill pinched up a little black snuff and with his thumb deftly pushed some into each of his nostrils while snuffing repeatedly as he kept his dark, watery, bloodshot eyes on me. I was so fascinated that I had to gaze with wide-open eyes and mouth. Nobody else in Thorp snuffed black stuff up into their nose, so Bill for that alone was worth knowing.

Bill got done snuffing, then perked up and said, "Say, Chub, what else you got on the program today?"

"Nothing I know of."

"Then, I'll tell you what. See that brand new pick and shovel that just came in? They're what they dug gold with up on the Klondike. Gus ordered them. He's waiting up on his place now so's he can dig up the richest vein of gold ore there is in Joe Watt Canyon — quick as he gets them. Say, Chub, do us a favor. Go ask your pa what if you'n me'll take this pick and shovel along with some other stuff up to Gus. You know how Gus is. He'll give the lot of us a share of his gold mine."

"What about Mama? Can she get a share of it?"

"Why, she'll get the fattest share of all. All she's got to do is send Gus a loaf or two of that bread she baked yesterday. Topped with a bit a dark tree honey, Gus'll think it's the tastiest grubstake a miner ever eat. A miner don't mind giving you a share of his mine for grubstaking him. You and me'll take Gus a dozen chops, two each for everybody, offa that shoat Johnnie butchered yesterday. Gus'll think that's grubstake enough for one day. Tell your pa, being as Happy's got a bruised foot, I'll hire a rig at the livery stable. And besides delivering Gus his Klondike pick and shovel, I'll work next Sunday to make up. Tell him that. Eh?"

I ran up to the front of the store and gave the news to my dad, making it sound as urgent as I could.

"Well, I guess so," he said. "I knew Bill'd be up to something like this. Go ask Mama first though. See what she says. I'll ask her, too."

Mama said she'd send Gus a couple of loaves of bread and two apple pies with them. She could bake extra to make up for it.

I ran along with Bill to the livery stable. He went to the house and soon returned with Mr. Newman. After a while

Mr. Newman led from inside the stable a sleek black horse in shiny metal-studded harness. It made Happy, even when looking her best, seem pretty common. Soon the black horse, with Bill ahold of the reins, was hitched to a covered buggy, and I was sitting in its black leather upholstered seat beside Bill.

"Well, Chub, here we go. Giddap, you Midnight! This is all the same as London. It'd make Happy green with envy, seeing us in this swell outfit. Too bad it don't have no rubber tires on it. Next time we'll get a rig with them on, too. Here we're to the hitching rack. I'll tie Midnight to it while you run in and get that bread and apple pies. I'll go to Johnnie's and fetch the chops. Oh! We don't want to forget that pick and shovel. Thank heaven, here's your pa bringing them now."

In a short time Bill and I were on our way. Then — just in time — it came to me that when riding in a buggy with a folding top on it, Bill ought to wear his tall silk hat. So I said:

"You know that hat you brought from London in that leather box?"

"Of course. It took Thorp by storm. What about it?"

"Up there is a good place to wear it, I think."

"You mean up at Gus's?"

"Uh huh."

"Never thought of that. Maybe it is. It's a sin not to wear it any. It's there in the Taneum House so I'll go in and get it. You wait here."

Bill stepped down and tied Midnight to a telephone pole, then hurried into the Taneum House. Soon he was back with his very tall hard silk hat, jauntily perched atop his head. Even more than that he wore a black and red striped robe, nearly touching the ground. Two rows of huge white buttons ran from his neck halfway down.

"Is that what you wore in London, Bill?"

"Right you are, Chub. But nothing's too good for this occasion, aither." (When he got up and sat beside me, I felt like I was next to some king.) "Now we're off. Giddap, Midnight!" Bill commanded. "This'll be our first fling up Joe Watt Canyon, eh, Chub?"

"Yeah, this is what I like to do. Were there gold mines where you were in London, Bill?"

"Yes — well — I mean, uh — there were some. Not enough to go around. That's why I came here. Up in these mountains is where they are. I bet Gus knows a *dozen* gold mines. It's a jolly good thing we fetched that pick and shovel for him to dig with."

We were soon moving along the road that led from the village past Mason's and Clyburn's farms, under the flume, then through the gully leading to the road that would take us past other farms on up to Joe Watt Canyon. As Midnight trotted, his steel shoes now and then hit a rock, causing it to spark. The buggy springs took up the jolts as the steel-clad wheels ground over the bared, often loose rocks. I looked up at Bill and felt good to see the protection and ornament the buggy top provided him in his silk hat and striped gown. Thorp was lucky that he came, I thought. When we got to Mason's barn, there was Johnnie running out waving at us.

"Hurry up, want to see something, come in here!" he shouted. The buggy stopped. I got down and followed Johnnie. He led me to a tall fence made of heavy boards spaced a foot apart, then motioned me to look inside the corral.

I had seen Mason's Jersey bull more than once inside his corral and was always thankful for the strong fence between us. He never seemed to care for anyone, and to show it he pawed the ground and bellowed and menaced with his solid sharp horns. Today his bellow did not sound so threatening.

It was agonized. Then I saw why. Securely bound by rope and flattened against the opposite fence, like a cardboard ox plastered to the wall, was Mason's Jersey bull. Near his tail was Alfred ahold of the rope end, leaning back to keep it tight. At the bull's head was Johnnie's dad, gritting his teeth as he sawed with might and main on a horn. So much blood was spurting I could not tell where it came from, but there on the ground was one horn — then two. When the bull was at last untied, he only stood with lowered head, not bellowing or pawing the ground, as blood spurted from holes where his horns had been.

My attention had been held so much on the horn operation that I hadn't noticed Mason's big sorrel workhorse laid out flat in one corner of the corral. Johnnie lamented:

"That's the bullet hole where Papa shot Jack after Dickens rammed his horns clear into Jack's belly!"

I could see the bullet hole and two wounds in the big, swollen belly and something oozing out of them. That was enough for me. I turned to see where Bill was. He had driven up behind me and had seen all that happened. I crawled up into the buggy beside him, relieved to get back on the road again. Midnight eagerly trotted away from the bloody scene.

Bill reached inside his robe and drew out a big white handkerchief. He dabbed his eyes and sniffed a few times. "That were horrible, weren't it, Chub?" he blubbered.

"Yeah, Mr. Mason was sure mad at that bull it looked like. But the horse got it worse than the bull."

"Mason is to blame. Leaving them in the same corral. Just imagine! Anyone oughter know a bull don't want any horse in with him. Now he's got no horns. Nothing to defend himself with. What if another bull comes in there with horns to fight him? Oh, Chub, I can't stand to think what would happen to that poor bull without no horns." Bill dabbed his eyes and sniffed again, but at last got composed enough to put his handkerchief back inside his robe.

"Bill, can that horse ever get up again?"

"Not with a bullet in his brain . . . poor thing. Well, here we are about to pass under the flume. It's sure leaky today. This road is a lake. It's a long way from where Tommie fell in that day, but it's where they found him. Right up there —" (Bill reached for his handkerchief again.) "My Tommie's back in London same age as —"

"Why can't he come here, Bill?"

"Well, Chub, I guess we'd better get along here. Got a long way to go to get to Gus's." He sniffed a few times more.

"Bill, could I drive Midnight once?"

"Oh, I fancy he'd go for that. Eh, Midnight? Here, take the reins. Careful now, we don't want to scare him into running away. Keep your eyes peeled out there in front of him. You daren't look to one side or t'other while holding them reins."

I firmly held a rein in each hand and kept my eyes glued to the road directly in front of Midnight. But that still left me with more side vision than Bill could guess I had. It was enough to let me detect him bringing from inside his robe a small, round not square, shiny container. He kept it mostly covered with his hands, but I could glimpse something white when it opened. Then he put his thumb and finger to his nostrils. I turned my head enough to see he was snuffing up some white stuff.

"Chub, don't mind me none. You got to keep your eyes out front. It got time to take a dose of this medicine for my headache. It'll make me fit as a fiddle in no time at all. It's the doctor's orders. Watch your driving now."

I was glad when we passed Catlin's place and after that came to Prater's. I couldn't wait to get to Gus's though. Bill had been quiet. I had wished he'd start talking, which was what he soon did.

"Well, Chub, my boy, old Bill feels on top of the world again. Nothing like a dose of that medicine to tone him up good. Pon my word, you're driving today better'n them London cabbies do.

> *Once I was ridin with a cabby*
> *Down that Piccadilly Avenue.*
> *I said don't get so darned all quabby*
> *My Thorp boy could show you what to do.*

"Gee, Bill, you're better'n Miss Love sayin things."

"Why not, Chub. I been in college a good bit, learnin to be a poet, you know."

"Is that what a poet says?"

"Righto, Chub. Righto. People like Keats or maybe Poe. They always talked like that."

"Do you know some more?"

"Heavens yes, Chub. I could think up poetry for us all the way to Gus's — and back. Used to make my living that way. But it's a lot easier getting it from a gold mine. By the way, Chub, how'd you like to have a team of Shetland ponies — you know, with a cart?"

"Who'd get it for me?"

"Why the best friend you have — next to your mother, of course, or maybe your father. The first thing I'm going to do with some of them gold nuggets is buy you a pair of black and white Shetlands, pulling a cart the kids can ride in. That's the kind of sport I am. Nothing's too good for Bill Nightingale's friends. Just you wait and see."

"Gee! When do I get them ponies?"

"Soon as we get to Gus's and dig enough of that gold to

bring back. He won't mind us taking that much, seeing all that he'll have left. Gus ain't no big spender."

Bill got quiet and took the reins from me, for we had come to a winding, narrow, steep road. Big pine trees grew on both sides of the road until we reached a clearing where an unpainted house and barn stood.

"Is that Gus's place?" I asked.

"No, this is where Meadowbird lives. There, he's coming from the barn now — probably wants a word with us."

Mr. Meadowbird wore blue overalls and jumper and had on an ordinary black felt hat with brim bent down in front. His sandy mustache — unlike most — was not tobacco-stained. His blue eyes were sharper than Bill's brown ones.

"Good morning, Mr. Meadowbird. You're looking fit'n fine this morning." (Bill had set his hat on the seat between us.)

"Yes, it's as good a morning as any. Praise the Lord, through whose mercy we live to enjoy it. You on your way up to see Gus?" Mr. Meadowbird sounded as though he might doubt we would ever find any trace of Gus. "His place is the one up the trail a quarter of a mile or so. Nothing after it but trees and *ferocious* animals."

"Have you seen Gus lately?" Bill asked.

"Can't say that I have. His wife's been here lately. Never knew she was back till she come screaming down here last night. Woke me up from a sound slumber. I caught her chopping on one of my best apple trees. She tried to claim I stole it from her. Why, she never had a tree to her name other'n a pine or a fir. When she come at me with that axe, I got on the other side of my door quick as lightning. There's a strong bolt on it. Praise the Lord! And when I slid it over, it held. Amen!"

"Did Gus's wife go back home?"

"Probably did. I rode down to Kane's this morning and phoned in for them to come and get her. They'll probably be along here this evening, praise the Lord."

"Oh, that's a shame," Bill, shaking his head and tsking, said. "Poor soul never got over losing her little Laurie." He drew out his handkerchief seeming to need it more than ever. Then, slapping Midnight with a rein and giving Mr. Meadowbird a wave, he started us on the final lap to Gus's place. The road got rougher than ever and more uphill, but Midnight was determined and soon brought us to another clearing with buildings that looked newer than Meadowbird's.

I was afraid we might meet Mrs. Floe with her axe, but I brightened up to see that Arthur and George were up near the squatty log barn playing horseshoes. We stopped near the door of an unpainted, shiplap-sided house. Gus had done a neat job in building it, though it seemed too small for a whole family. I knew from listening to Gus that it was where little Laurie had died one winter when the snow was deep. There was a movement at the window and I saw it must be Mrs. Floe peering out. Her large black eyes had a wildness in them and she stared as though afraid of us.

Opening onto a wide porch was a doorway that Gus soon appeared in, smiling as usual. He showed there was nothing to worry about as he raised his hands in a welcoming gesture. On the side of the buggy next to Gus, Bill stiffly held the reins up as he posed for Gus to see him in his hat and gown. Gus looked unbelieving for a moment, then shook his head as though giving up and motioned toward the barn. His pipe was in his hand.

"Vhy you don't put dat ol nag in de barn. He's needin some hay dis time. Eh, heh. Maybe you vant to hang dat hat and oder ting you're varing on de harness peg out dere, your

English mayesty." Gus bowed as he relieved himself of those words.

"I say you Scandihoovian limey, how dare you insult my London habiliment, hinting I should lodge it in your backwoods barn! Where's your clothes closet?"

"Vell, your mayesty, I'm apoloyizing for dat. Next time I'm packing dem boards up dis mountain for making close closet. Eh, heh. Dis time I'm needing tings like flour and a fork a hay for dat nag."

"Then show us your spring so's this blooded animal can fresh himself up with a little *aqua pura* after climbing this mountain with that pick and shovel for you."

"You brung it?"

"Indeed we did. It's time some gold was coming down out of this canyon."

"Vait inside dere den vhile I unhitch dis nag and vater and feed him. Ve havin some hot biscuits for dinner."

I got down out of the buggy and ran up to see Arthur and George. I could not wait to go exploring among the big trees that were close around us. The smell and dampness of them put new life into me and made me feel fit enough even to want to take Arthur on for a game of horseshoes. But I found his horseshoes not to my liking, so I asked him what else we could do. I saw that Gus and Bill were unhitching Midnight.

"Wanta go see our mine?"

"Sure," I said eagerly.

Arthur took off up the hill, closely followed by George and me. After passing some big trees, Arthur stopped at a hole I feared might be a bear's cave. It was in the side of a room-high, steep bank of brownish-streaked earth. Arthur dropped onto his hands and knees and crawled inside it. George followed him, leaving me all alone. Concerned, I stood peering at the black hole they had vanished into.

George soon came crawling out, then Arthur came dragging a short-handled shiny spade.

"What's in there?" I asked.

"We're digging for gold and silver," Arthur informed me. "Dad's got a bigger mine with *real gold* in it down that way. He don't know where this'n is."

"How can I see what's in there?"

"Follow George. Go on, George, show him. I'll dig some more. There ain't no animals in there this time."

It seemed an awfully long way into the scary darkness and I was glad when George stopped and I could feel room by twisting round to sit beside him. I could see out. Arthur was in the light and I thought it gave him a halo — I was that glad to see him. He crawled a little way toward us dragging the spade.

"Here looks like a lucky place to dig. There's some shiny stuff there," Arthur announced.

He began carving into the side of the tunnel between him and us. Soon he had a pile of dirt a foot high in front of George and me. He kept on carving and digging into the side and sometimes at the top. I heard him say:

"There's gotta be some gold here somewhere!" Sweat was dripping from his face.

Then I saw dirt in front of us quickly pile higher. A lot higher. Silently it built up like wheat spilling on the ground from a threshing machine spout. I couldn't utter a sound. Suddenly a mass of dirt let loose, and then all was black. I felt George moving, but I froze, too scared to move. What could I do? I wanted to cry and tried to yell, but could only make a weak noise. I tried to claw the dirt. I tried to kick it. Nothing did any good. It got hot and I began to shake and sweat. I could not feel George moving anymore. I wanted to sleep, and got more sleepy, more all the . . . .

I opened my eyes in a ray of light. I felt George move.

Part of the light was blocked out. Then there was more light. Soon it looked big enough to crawl through. It got bigger. I could see Arthur digging for all he was worth. At last, George crawled out and I was right after him. To be in the daylight again was like in heaven.

"Oh boy!" Arthur exclaimed. "It's lucky you got outa there! We better get to the house. Don't tell Dad you was in there. Hurry up, follow me."

Happy to have escaped from the black hole, I ran after Arthur and got to the house just in time to see Gus and Bill leaving for the gold mine. Gus carried his new shovel. Bill followed with pick and unlit lantern. We boys stayed close behind them. Bill now wore his flat, visored cap, a red plaid jacket and checked gray trousers. Gus wore his dark hat with narrow turned-up brim and blue waist overalls. His pipe was lit.

After tripping as fast as I could uphill and down, my legs complained so I wanted to stop. Then a large square hole in the side of a hill, framed by small tree trunks, came into view. Gus walked to it and stopped. So did we. He lit the lantern.

"Vell, Bill, now I'm showing ye inside all dis mine. Eh, heh. Not room for boys dis time. It's good dey stay here."

"Uh-uh-uh, you mean in — in.... How far is it Gus? Possibly I can see from *here*."

"You not scared unrolling dat linen for ladies. Vhy you scared a gold mine? Not even bears in dere. I show ye."

"Well, uh-uh-uh — I suppose it's up to you, Gus. That lantern will brighten things up a bit, won't it?"

I saw Bill draw the little round metal box from his breast pocket and open it with trembling hand as he followed Gus into the mine. We sat down on a log to wait. At last Gus, with lantern in one hand and a chunk of rock in the other, appeared smiling at the mine entrance. Then came Bill with a chunk of rock in each hand and an expression to say he had discovered the mother lode no less. Gus blew out the lantern and found a small black object in his front pocket. When he opened it, I saw glass. Bill, with his hands still full, came close to Gus.

Gus tightly closed one eye as he peered learnedly through the glass at the rock. He smiled and nodded repeatedly, then gave the glass and rock to Bill who had set his rocks on the ground. Bill imitated Gus to perfection as he nodded his head and grunted knowing agreement with Gus's assay. Still nodding and smiling, Bill handed the glass and rock back to Gus.

"Now you seen dat gold outa dat mine. Eh, heh. Time to eat. I tink Effie baking dem biscuits, also frying dose pork shops. Come vit me to house. Eh, heh. Ve drink gallon milk Gus got pay for milking Thompson cows dis morning."

We soon got into the house where Effie stood at the stove frying the chops. She wore a sack-type dress of mixed-gray calico. Her braided dark brown hair hung down her back. She did not turn from the stove. There was a tin plate with a knife and fork set for each of us on a brown and black oilcloth-covered table. Gus pointed to a bench at one side so Bill and I sat on it. Three sat opposite us. Our backs were to the stove. A tin plate of chops and a granite kettle of boiled potatoes were set on the table. I ate some of both, relishing every bite. Then came biscuits, and brown milk gravy from the pork chop skillet. I ate a biscuit straight and my mouth watered for more like it, but I could not resist putting gravy on the next one.

The three pieces of sharp-edged, rough-surfaced rock brought from the mine were each about the size of Gus's fist. They were laid on the end of the table close to me, so I could see that they were of mixed color with many brilliant specks in some places. As soon as the table was cleared, Gus took out his glass, picked out a rock and began examining it in the manner he had used at the mine.

"What d'you see there, Gus?" Bill sounded out of breath.

"Vell, she looks wery good. Better dan I tought. No tellin how much a dis yunk is buried under dat mountain."

"You own it all, don't you, Gus?"

"Dat's vone ting I know. Gus owns it. It yust takes hard vork diggin it."

"Gus, what do you reckon that vein amounts to altogether? How many dollars a gold?"

"Vell, let me tink. Got a pencil? Roll up dat oilclot so's ye can figure on table board. Ye're smarter'n ol Gus doin ritmetic. Before de mast dere vas no vay a learnin ritmetic."

"About how big do you reckon that vein is, Gus?" Bill sounded eager to hear.

"Oh, I tink maybe tree yards tick." Gus spread his arms sideways. "How deep? Oh — I tink ten yards." Gus raised one hand high and lowered the other to indicate depth.

"Only *one vein* is that big?"

"Yah, yah, dat not wery big for gold wein up dese mountains."

"Let's see here now. Ten by three, that's thirty yards every . . . . Say, Gus, how many dollars a gold d'you reckon there's in a yard a that vein?"

"Oh, I tink maybe hundred, sometimes ninety, sometimes little more. Dat's all."

"Holy o mackinaw!" Bill lowered his voice way down, but sitting close to him, I could hear, "Three thou . . . . Think a that — one thousand dollars every foot . . . . By the way, Gus, how long is that vein? How far down d'you think it goes?"

"Oh, maybe only a mile, dis vone." Gus seemed little interested in Bill's figuring.

Bill's voice was no more than a whisper. "Incredible!

Five thousand two hundred times one thousand . . . . That's over five million dollars in only one vein! No tellin how many veins he's got up here."

"Effie, you vant you should gif Mr. Nightingale more coffee, maybe, huh. Dat figurin vares somebody out."

"Yes, but gold's all he wants and the Lord put me here to keep this gold for Judgment Day. Nobody can take the Lord's gold. He told me this morning. You got to leave it for Him. Don't you know I'm the Angel of the Lord coming back here to save you?" The serious tone of Effie's voice was like I imagined the Lord would sound.

"Dat's right, Effie. Ve keeping all dat gold here. Ve only selling Mr. Nightingale a share. All dat gold is for de Lord."

I turned and saw that Effie was nodding as she went back to her dishpan on the stove.

"Say, Gus, she's all mixed up, ain't she? Fancy her thinkin she's the 'Angel of the Lord.' This mountain air will fix her up though. Make her right as a fiddle. How'm I going to know I got a share in your mine?"

"Dat's easy. You got a pencil? Write on piece a paper. Like dat vone. Yust say: 'De bearer, Bill Nightingale, is owning a share a Gus Floe's gold mine and gets all de mineral rights to boot.' Vhat day is it? Put dat down, too."

"I got it down here, Gus, just like you said. But I won't let you give it to me for nothin. Just because I'm your friend. This is a business deal, you know. Nothing else. Name your price, whatever it is, so long as it don't break me."

"Vell, I tink maybe dis time, six dollars. You got dat much?" Gus looked hopefully at Bill's pocket.

"Got it to a T, Gus. Got it right here." Bill reached into his pocket as Gus watched with aroused interest. One silver dollar and a five dollar gold piece quickly appeared in Bill's hand and soon were deep in Gus's pocket. . . . "Here, Gus, put your X on this paper."

"Yah, dat's . . . it. Now you owning dat share of . . . vhat ve calling him . . . 'Million Dollar Gold Mine'?"

"That's splendid, Gus. Think of that! 'The Million Dollar Gold Mine'! How many million did I figure was in there? Never mind, Gus. One's enough for now. You know where to find me. We've talked business enough for one day. Now we can visit — unless you have to get busy right off with that Klondike pick and shovel."

"Bright and early in de morning I'm digging dat gold I tink. Dis time I'm needing smoke dis pipe." Gus held the unlit pipe with his teeth as he found a knife and a plug of tobacco in his front pocket, then opened the knife and began to slice the tobacco. It was hard for me to wait until he had crumbled the slices in his palm, filled the pipe and lit it. The smoke that bathed his weathered face smelled good to me.

"How d'you and your nearest neighbor make out, Gus? He talks like he has a direct connection with the 'throne of God.' "

"Yah, dat's him. Vit him down dere I ain't got to have no preacher up here, I tink. You seen his apple trees?"

"Sure, he pointed them out to us, Gus."

"Yah, but he can't selling dose apples. Too many apple trees. So last vall he telling me, 'Gus, you like some a dem apples? Help yourself. Dere's plenty for you. Fill up some gunny sacks so dey not rotting on ground.' "

"That was right down neighborly of Mr. Meadowbird, Gus."

"Yah, dat's vhat I vas tinking. So I'm taking down dere two gunny sacks. I'm not filling dem up. Yust half full, ye see. Anyvay I'm tanking him like I'm saying, 'How much I owe ye Mr. Meadowbird?' . . . 'Aw, let's see, dat's not much ye got, Gus. Oh, uh, how bout two bits a sack, Gus? Den ve call it fair and square.' "

That made Bill laugh in a way to encourage Gus to tell more — I could tell by his faster puffing. "Vhen I'm coming in dis walley dat year I'm asking old Veed down dere for a yob . . . ."

As much as I liked to hear Gus's yarns I wanted more to explore his virgin pine woods. Arthur and George had been in them many times. Now they were wrapped up listening to their dad. So was Bill. I slipped outside and ran toward the thickest woods, hoping Bill wouldn't miss me. I was soon out of sight. It was a rare feeling among the lofty pines whose smooth trunks were bigger than barrels. The dewy air was richly scented with turpentine and pine oil. A few deep breaths sent me farther into the woods, wanting more of the refreshing, resiny odor.

It was getting hard to tell one pine trunk from another, and the farther I went the bigger they looked. A gray squirrel with the longest and bushiest tail I'd ever seen appeared on a branch of one tree and then ran down its trunk . On the ground he ambled up a slight knoll, going slow enough for me to think I could catch up with him. But he kept the same distance ahead with no effort, while I got out of wind. It was easier going down the far side of the knoll, but I never got close to the squirrel. He ran up a trunk and disappeared among the branches. I turned around and started back to Gus's. But none of the trees looked familiar so I took another direction hoping to find trees I had seen before. But I didn't. I tried in another direction. Nothing looked familiar there either. I kept peering through the trees — desperate for a glimpse of Gus's house or his mine or of anything except the leather-brown and black-creviced bark of more pine tree trunks.

I tramped until I could barely go. Then downgrade.

Everywhere the trees were the same. At last there was a meadowy clearing that I thought must be near Gus's. When I tried to run across it I stumbled and fell. My knee hurt. Stickers pierced my fingers. After that, it felt almost home-like back among the trees where I could sit on a root and rest my back against smooth bark. But there was no sign of water or anything to eat. It seemed a long time since I had listened to Gus talking to Bill. I was now far away from their voices and too tired to get up or keep my head from nodding.

When I opened my eyes and could see only dimly through the trees, I jumped up scared and ran toward the lightest point — faint as it was. I tripped and fell, hurting my hand, but got right up and ran on. No one was there to hear my cries. At last I got out from among the trees into less dark-ness. Just ahead, I spied a slithering on the ground that startled me. It looked like a snake, then I saw it was running water and I hurried to it. I found a shallow, gravelly-bot-tomed pool the size of a tin dishpan. Water trickled out of a steep bank into it. I ducked my face and drank. It was cool and sweet, like milk. I stretched out on a smooth spot, quite contented, until I saw it was the moon giving the light. That meant it was night, maybe midnight. It was a scary dis-covery. Being hungry made it worse so I got up to look for something to eat. Up the bank I saw tiny umbrellas that looked more tender than pine cones. It was easy to pull one up. It oozed juice and was so velvety that I started to put it whole into my mouth, but I stopped scared stiff on hearing a sharp crackle, then a scream of words behind me:

"Spit that out!"

There was nothing I had to spit out *yet,* and though hardly able to move a finger, I turned my head enough to see someone in a long dress coming toward me. I had never seen a ghost and I shook all over in seeing one now. Then to my unbounded joy I saw it was Effie, mother of Arthur and George.

"Don't you know them toadstools'll kill you? The Angel of the Lord knows."

"Ain't they good to eat? I'm hungry!"

"Course they're not. Here, I brung you one a old Meadowbird's apples. Gus bought it. It's a big'n. Eat it while I get me a drink outa that spring. The Lord's the one who put it all the way up here for Effie."

I attacked the apple with a gusto sharpened by having failed to fill up on toadstools. Before I was done with the apple, Effie guided me to a big tree within sight of the spring and the moon.

"Right here's where we got to stay till it's daylight. Then the Angel of the Lord knows the way back home." Effie sat on the ground under a tree. "Sit down here," she commanded.

It was darker than ever so I found comfort in sitting as close as I could get to her. "How long will it be dark?" I asked.

"The Lord makes it dark and the Lord makes it light. It's up to Him. He shows me the way besides. That's how I got here. I'm the Angel of the Lord. They'll find out. The ones who tried to burn me up will."

I heard something *snap* and in the moonlight saw an object moving near the trees beyond the spring. I stiffened and held my breath.

"What's that?" I asked weakly.

"Oh, that's that old Longtooth what lives back up there. He has to get hisself a drink once in a while — same as us."

"Will he hurt us?"

"Never has hurt nobody. Black bears don't much care to eat humans. Less they're starvin."

"What if he's starvin?"

"He knows I'm the Angel of the Lord come back to earth. I'll scare him off same as I scared Meadowbird."

I watched nervously as the bear ambled to the spring and lapped up water. Then suddenly he raised his head looking in our direction. I froze with terror, expecting him to jump at us, but he turned away and, no too soon for me, disappeared.

"He skedaddled outa here soon as he seen the Angel of the Lord. We'll lay down here and sleep for a time. He knows better'n to bother round here now."

My back being next to Effie kept me from freezing all over, so long as I didn't budge a bit. I liked being awake, feeling her warmth, and felt too scared to let myself fall asleep anyway. . . . But now my back was cold. I opened my eyes. It was not pitch dark anymore and I saw her standing up.

"Now we can see. Come on."

I jumped up and followed as Effie hurried through the gloom and dimness. Light was filtering through the pine-needled branches, and it kept getting easier to see. The tree trunks looked the same as the ones I had once passed. I worried when she stopped and turned her head as though sensing some danger. Whatever she suspected, she walked in the direction she'd turned to. We met Gus and Bill. They shook their heads as though unbelieving and looked haggardly at me. Effie turned and continued through the forest, silently followed by Gus, Bill and me. I was becoming more scared of getting out of the forest than staying in it. With good reason, for we were no sooner in sight of Gus's house than I saw Papa and Mama sitting in our buggy, looking as tired out as I felt. After Gus went and talked to them, both stepped down onto the ground. Mama hurried to Effie, hugged her and kissed her on the cheek. Papa shook her hand and patted her shoulder. Then Mama spoke to Bill.

"Mr. Nightingale, you know I trusted you'd watch Gordon up here, especially after you promised me so faithfully that you would. This has been a terrible worry, but thanks to Mrs. Floe, Gordon has been found. I'm sure you feel bad enough, so we'll just be thankful that nothing worse happened."

"Yes, ma'am. He got out of sight here before I knew it. What a night!"

The grown-ups kept on talking, Mr. Meadowbird among them. I sidled away, but not too far. Then I saw a one-seated, light spring wagon near the barn. As I gazed wonderingly at it a man and woman came out of the house. They walked toward us and I saw a big bright star on the man's chest. I had seen him in Thorp taking a man to jail. Maybe he was after me. I wanted to run to Mama and Papa, but stood scared stiff as the man wearing the star and the tall woman wearing a hard-brimmed black hat pierced by long pins walked past me to the group of grown-ups. All I could do was stand and wait, hardly daring to breathe. Then Mama came and took my hand. We walked to the buggy where Papa was sitting and got in beside him.

"Gordon, that's the sheriff and his wife," Papa said. "We'll wait till Bill gets hitched up so we can stay together."

"Gordon," Mama said, "we know you did not mean to get lost and worry us half to death. We are thankful you were found and it will make you more careful after this. We would be disappointed if Mr. Meadowbird had not also appreciated Mrs. Floe's bringing you back. He said it was his fault the sheriff had to come. The sheriff said he could see Mrs. Floe could take care of herself now. Just think, on account of her finding you, they made a trip all the way up here for nothing. If you hadn't got lost, I'm afraid they would be taking her away again." Suddenly Mama leaned forward and exclaimed, "Oh my goodness! Now what!"

It sounded like a hard slap on someone's cheek and I was startled to hear Effie cry out and then see her whirl around and dash toward the nearest trees. The sheriff's wife, moving even quicker, grabbed Effie's arm. Effie turned and kicked with one foot then the other, so hard it must've cracked both shins of her pursuer. By that time the sheriff had come to his wife's aid and together they struggled to subdue Effie. It made me cry to see her laid on the ground with her hands manacled behind her back.

"Oh, mercy me," Mama moaned, as shaking her head she stepped down on the ground and went straight to Effie. Then on her knees Mama began smoothing Effie's forehead and hair. I sat in clear view of Effie's appalling misery, crying so I couldn't be of any help to her. The sheriff's wife, though, stood near while the sheriff went to hitch up his team. He then drove the wagon close beside Effie. When the sheriff got down from the wagon, I saw he carried a kind of canvas coat with very long sleeves. Papa and Gus began talking and motioning very earnestly to him, but the sheriff only shook his head.

As Bill stood near the wagon, I saw his handkerchief come from the pocket inside his coat and go to his face. Bill could plead like no one else, so my hope rose high when he then approached the sheriff. But the sheriff only shook his head and, most noticeably with it, the commanding tall wide hat he wore. Nothing could be worse, I thought, than having him with his holstered, steely six-shooter and that flapping thing in his hand after you. His long-hatpinned wife in her divided black skirt — fit for breaking horses to ride — would be just as bad, I shuddered and shrank to think.

Mama kept trying to sooth Effie, who continued to talk and moan. Bill had gone beyond the wagon where he was pushing something up into his nostrils. He had tearfully given up on the sheriff who was now down on one side of

Effie with his wife on the other. They freed Effie's hands of the manacles, without releasing them, and together began forcing her hands deep into the long sleeves. Mama got up and came back toward our buggy. There were tears in her eyes, running down her cheeks. Then I saw Arthur at the open door of their house, wringing his hands. Poor George came rushing toward us, shouting:

"Get out of here! Go on home! You don't have to be here! They'll leave Mama go now." Then he broke down crying and ran back inside the house.

The sheriff and his wife had tightened the jacket around Effie, whose hands were inside the far-extended sleeves, crossed and bound against her body. There was nothing she could do but kick and moan. The most that Papa and Gus could now do was to help lift Effie up and gently lay her in the wagon.

When the sheriff drove his wagon past us, I could hardly look. When I did look to the bottom of it, I saw only Effie's mixed-gray calico dress that had seemed like heaven come to me when lost out there at that spring the night before. But now the wagon seat covered and kept me from seeing her face even once again. I had believed she *was* the Angel of the Lord as she had told me.

At the sound of Gus's voice, I turned toward his house and saw him on the porch, his arms filled with a heavy, many-colored, pieced quilt. His repeated call of "Vait!" caused the sheriff to bark "Whoa!" about three lengths of the wagon from us. Gus hurried to it and, stepping up on the wheel, spread the quilt over Effie. After carefully tucking it in around her, he gently reached under the seat to her face, but there was little time and as soon as he stepped down the wagon moved on. With pain written on his lined, weathered face, Gus slowly turned and walked back into his house.

I could see Papa and Mama were as stunned and grieved as I was. After a while, Bill looking sad drove by and waved to us. His silk hat sat on the seat beside him where I had sat coming up. I knew he had that little round box tucked inside his coat somewhere and could use it freely on his way home. I hoped he'd have no more need of his handkerchief.

Arthur and George were inside, too; so Papa and Mama said they would go see them awhile and for me to stay in the buggy. As I waited, the early morning sun rose and its warm rays shone cheerily on Gus's front porch. They shone on the green weeds and grass around the house and on the tall pines behind it. They shone on the tiny pool of water at the nearby spring and on the barn. It seemed they were trying to make the clearing in the forest appear as cheerful and inviting as it had been the morning before. But it was not the same. After a long time, Papa and Mama solemnly came back and got in the buggy with me. Mama had brought two of Effie's biscuits, which she said I could eat on the way home.

Chapter 9

THORP CELEBRATES
THE FOURTH

On the back porch where I slept, only heavy muslin hung between me and the chickens so that their clucking and singing in chorus cheerily woke me. It was morning of the Fourth of July at last. The sun's early rays seeped through the muslin, which didn't flap a bit, meaning the old Kittitas breeze had finally quit. When it didn't blow, there was a lot more to celebrate. I heard a firecracker go off so there was no time to waste in getting outside. But I was hungry for breakfast. Another firecracker! I had to get outside. Mama would let me eat later — yeah, like fun. I heard her coming.

"Oh, you're up, Gordon. Are you glad this is the Fourth of July? It's a beautiful day, too. Come on and get washed. Breakfast is ready. The other boys are eating theirs."

Mama poured cold water from the bucket, then hot water out of the teakettle into the washpan for me. She made me put on my school clothes even though I protested, knowing Frank and Bob would wear overalls. I was soon at the dining table eating French toast and drinking rich Jersey milk. But I was in a hurry to get outside, so I gulped down the rest of my breakfast and headed for the back door, grabbing my cap gun and caps on the way. Since no one else was using the torpedo cane, I took it with some flat blue tablets that exploded in the iron end when hit on a rock. Exploding it always stung my ankles, but it never seemed to bother Frank and Bob. I ran across the street and found them beside a boxcar where they'd promised to be.

"Here's Chub now," Frank greeted me. "Did these fire-crackers wake you up? Hey! Gee that's good! You brought that torpedo shooter. Just what I like. When you pound it, it sounds like dynamite explodin."

"Yeah, here, take it."

"Look, Chub. Me'n Frank's been blastin stuff with these firecrackers. We cover em up with dirt and cinders, all ex-cept the fuzee. Then we light it. It's a lot more fun than just lettin them go off by themselves. Say, let's hear you shoot some caps in that gun."

"Yeah, I'm going to. Here it goes."

We managed to make a lot of noise, but a freight train roared by to drown it out for a while. It seemed too bad to me that the men running it could not celebrate the Fourth of July in Thorp like we were doing.

Bob said, "Look! There goes Bill Wilbur and Joe Keene. They've got a keg of beer ditched in the millrace gettin it cool. I seen them and Oat Bradshaw haulin it in a wheel-barrow last night. I spied on them. Les follow them, so's they don't see us. I know where. It's pretty near to them big pine trees where the celebratin's goin to be. Come on, les go. We kin come back and see the parade when it goes down there."

We ran across the railroad and on into the livery stable's high-fenced driveway. We heard Newman's hydraulic ram go *cachunk . . . cachunk . . . cachunk* as it forced water through a pipe into a high wooden tank. The ram was set down in a gravelly cavity left one year by the flood. On other days we had gone there to watch the ram spouting water. Now we hurried on to cross the planked wagon bridge over the millrace. On our left was the path that wound through the brush to our swimming hole. We could go there other days. Today we wanted to see a keg of beer get tapped on the millrace bank as a way to celebrate the Fourth, so we turned right. Near the millrace was open pasture, so to keep out of sight we followed Bob, pushing through the brush and trees growing along the bank. Before long, Bob signaled for us to stop. We were hidden where we could both see and hear Bill and Joe, who were soon joined by Oat Bradshaw and Alfred Fairwood.

"Joe, let's get er out here and punch this spigot in er," Bill urged. "I get terrible thirsty livin in that dry hole of a Thorp. Been waitin for this for a year, seems like."

"Me too," Joe said. "Roll er out here and stand er on end. That's it. Now to lay er in the crotch of these two boulders . . . . There, she's ready to draw. Boy, this oughta be good and cool after that water runnin on it since yesterday."

"Yeah," Oat agreed. "This is the way to celebrate the Fourth. I ain't had any cool beer for a month."

"Me either," Alfred exclaimed. "Let's at er. Now who in the nation brought these crocks? I know. It was you, Bill, cause I seen em at your place. They're the only fit kind of mug to drink suds from."

The talking went on, and they all laughed after Joe, in a low voice, told a story. We waited, not daring to make any sound.

"Let's pull straws to see who draws his mug full first," Joe said. "Shortest one wins. Here you are . . . . You got it, Alfred. Hop to it. I'm dry as the tail end of a thirsty rattler."

"Well, I'll be donkey's uncle. You mean I won somethin."

"Don't get your nose in the foam, Alfred. Blow er off so it don't drown you," Bill joshed.

"He's got his . . . . Say, that beer ain't got a lot of foam on it. Looks kinda pale-like. Must a got too cold. You try it, Bill," Oat urged.

"No, it's not foaming much and awful pale besides," Bill agreed as he drew his mug full. "Probably it'll taste good though."

In a minute all four had filled their mugs and stood ready to drink good health to each other. "Well, let's everybody take a yard-long swig," said Joe.

All four began to drink. But something was wrong. All but Alfred were spitting out their first mouthfuls.

"Well, I'll be a so-and-so! That's nothin but that wishy-washy creek water!" Oat exploded.

I was crouched behind Bob, and I thought he would bust trying to keep from laughing. Luckily, before he did laugh out loud, he turned around and stealthily crept back through the brush with Frank and me right on his tail. When at a safer distance, we stopped, and both Frank and Bob had to laugh until they shed tears.

"Don't tell anyone, Chub. You're in it now, same as us," Bob warned me. I knew what he meant.

We snuck back to the millrace bridge. The grove, where the day's celebration would be held, was not far away toward the river. Bill and his gang had not yet come in sight. We held a conference.

Frank said, "I know somethin. Ruby Jewel is barbecuin a whole cow for the celebration. A whole one! Let's go down there and see it."

We took off on a run and soon were in sight of "Ol' Ruby" standing there with a supposedly white bib apron over his blue overalls and gray shirt, and a floppy straw hat tilted back on his head. He had probably not shaved his dark whiskers for a week. A cloud of smoke rose round him as he began swabbing the beef with a dirty-looking greasy rag, tied on the end of a long stick. The carcass rested on several lengths of iron, laid across a deep pit dug in the ground with a wood fire glowing at the bottom of it. As Ruby walked around the carcass to swab it, he now and then dipped the rag into a pail of grease he carried. He finished his round and set his pail down, seeming glad to see us.

"Here I'm gittin beef barbed enough for a regiment and I ain't had no breakfast," Ruby drawled. "Ain't had no sleep neither. Been keepin this carcass smokin two days." Ruby came from the South where they knew how to barbecue. That was why they had gotten him to do it. "Chub, yuh reckon your ma'd have an extry slice or so a her bread she'd spare? If you'll run an fetch it, I'll fix it for you an her to get the juiciest hunks a this barbycue yuh ever seen."

Ruby looked to me like he had not slept for a week and needed something to eat. But his barbecue didn't seem to me like anything Mama would want a piece of. Me neither. Not when I knew she would bring fried chicken. But at least the ones who hired Ruby would like his cooking, I was sure. In the meantime I would feel important bringing him some bread for breakfast. So I started off.

"Wait, Chub. Take this lard pail and fetch a splash a coffee in it, won'tcha?"

With my mother's usual cooperation I managed to bring Ruby his breakfast. He had enough barbecued beef as he said for a regiment, but I guess it was all eaten because people came from far out in the country to a Fourth of July celebration at Thorp.

By the time Ruby had his breakfast, people in their rigs were coming over the millrace bridge to the picnic grounds. You could hear firecrackers going off far and near. But Frank and Bob and I had other interests. For one thing, we wanted to watch the band and whatever else there might be in the parade. It didn't take a lot of floats to make a parade spectacular in Thorp. After a while we heard the band coming. Those still at home in the village had already been able to see the parade. We ran to meet it.

In the lead came Wesley Weed's prancing iron-grey team, decorated in red, white and blue. Wesley held reins tight on them. On his hayrack — a platform about six by ten feet — were four bales of hay where several men sat blowing brass horns and Chet Ames was beating his drums. In a high-sided wagon bed following the band stood Mr. Dolby in his red, white and blue Uncle Sam costume. He held the handle of a wheelchair. Anna Warner, also dressed in Fourth of July bunting, was in it. Her smile could not conceal how pale she was. Then a hayrack coming on wagon wheels had the words MODERN WOODMEN on its side. There was action on it. Across the rack was laid a thick pine log on which Burt Hahn and Ed Bradshaw were slowly pulling a crosscut saw back and forth. Finally, there came Jack Mason pulling reins on his spanking bay team. There was bunting on the team and all over the hayrack. I knew the words on it — ROYAL NEIGHBORS OF AMERICA — for my mother was one of more than a dozen women sitting on the wagon. They were dressed all in white with silk scarves over their heads.

"Say, you guys," Frank exclaimed, "didja hear that *honk honk?* Must be Mr. Mundy comin in his automobile. No! Look at that red thing comin. It's big as a thrashing machine. Mr. Mundy's is black and twice as small as it."

"Yeah," Bob said, "but I can tell Mr. Mundy's sittin there holdin that wheel. I seen him before. That's him, all right. There, he honked again. Gee! Yuh never seen nothin like that so red all over. It's even shinier than a brand-new wagon box. Wouldn't it be keen to ride in the big seat, Chub?"

"But it's all full," I said.

"The back seat's full of flowers," Frank laughed. "That's the Mundy girls, Lily and Pansy and Daisy. The hired men call em the 'old maids.' That's Mrs. Mundy in front. Once I was at their place with my dad. Hear that horn honkin."

"What's that *chug-chug-chug* sound like anyway, I wonder?" Bob asked. "You can even smell the smoke comin out in back."

"Frank! Bob!" I exclaimed. "Look what's still coming."

"Oh, that's just them ol mules a Mundy's," Frank informed us. "Don't you member seein em hitched onto his black automobile?"

"Yeah," Bob agreed, "but them two mules couldn't never pull this great big red one. They're only pullin a buggy with George Fields in it, comin there."

The mule-drawn buggy passed by, and Frank and Bob and I followed it on to the picnic grounds where the automobile was stopped. George drove the mules on farther. Mr. Mundy was bent over beside the front end of his automobile turning fasteners. He then lifted the engine hood and folded it back.

Bob said, "Look, he's fixin some things inside there with a wrench and screwdriver."

Among others — also with mouths open — we stood staring. It was a sight to make even the oldest trees standing there stiffen up and stare.

"Look, he's wearin his long 'flour sack' duster," Frank whispered to us. "You know what that cap is he's wearin? It's his army cap. You kin tell by that flat place out in front he was in Lincoln's Army — I think. Wait till he takes that long coat off. He was a regular general. Got two of them things on his sleeve — pointed like a chicken coop roof."

Mr. Mundy folded down and fastened the engine hood. Then, after replacing his tools in the box on the running board, he took off his black gauntlets and duster, and laid them on the front seat. Mr. Lynn Pardee with white mustache and Mr. Tom Wilson with full gray beard, both wearing brass-buttoned coats and blue-tasseled braid on their darker-blue felt hats, came up close to Mr. Mundy and his flaming new automobile. Their apparel proclaimed that all three had been in the Union Army. We boys stood close enough to hear what they said.

"This is some contraption you got here, Luther," I heard Lynn Pardee say.

"Well, you know, we had quite a crop of hay last year, so I figured I'd spend some of it on foolishment. Besides, I needed something for them mules to do," Luther said laughingly. "That little old Rambler was getting to be no work for them at all."

"What kind of name does this'n have?" Lynn asked.

"Same as the little one — Rambler. Made by the same factory, they tell me. Likely it's the best there is made."

"Luther, what's that there leever stuck on the side there for?" Mr. Wilson asked.

"That's what you shift gears with. Say for instance, you want to back up, you slip it into that slot where I just put it. Then you want to go ahead — just slide it back into that slot. That's first gear. Now you're moving ahead so you shift across into this one, which is second gear, to get going faster. Then you can put her right ahead, like this, into high gear. Of course, you got to put the clutch out with that foot pedal every time you shift a gear."

"How fast does the danged thing travel, I wonder?" Mr. Wilson asked.

"Up to thirty-five miles in an hour," Mr. Mundy replied.

"Holy Moses, Luther! That's mighty nigh as far as North Yakima in an hour!" Mr. Wilson exclaimed. "It takes all day gettin there in a wagon."

"Luther, how in tarnation do them mules ever keep up with it?" Mr. Pardee demanded.

"Well, Lynn, they don't really keep up with it. They just catch up with it, generally," Mr. Mundy said with a laugh. "Here, Lynn, have an Owl on me. You couldn't smoke a cigar, could you, Tom, with that cud of Horseshoe salivering your mouth?"

Tom promptly unloaded a gob of tobacco juice on the ground to make room for the cigar being offered him.

"Luther, how much steam do you reckon this here autymobile's got without them mules hitched to it?" Tom asked, his mouth now emptied of juice.

"Well, boys, you won't believe this, but it's a fact," Mr. Mundy explained. "Under that little hood there is twenty — and I mean twenty! — horsepower feeding off a twelve-gallon tank of gasoline hid there."

Mr. Pardee kept shaking his head as he gazed at the front of the big red Rambler. "Well, Luther, I ain't one to deny it. They got it so you can talk to Chicago through a rig no bigger'n your hand. So I reckon they could put twenty horses to workin inside there without ever seein em."

"That's right, Lynn. Say, boys, you know I have to make a speech here today. But I'll tell you what. As soon as it's done, I'll give you a ride in this Rambler."

"Much obliged, Luther. You know well I'd be proud a that," Tom said. "The trouble is, today I promised to get the cows in early for Floyd so's he can get done milkin and come to the dance."

Lynn, gazing toward the merry-go-round, said casually, "I'd rather the other folks get the first chance, Luther. I can ride with you some other time."

"Bob, didja hear that? Maybe Mr. Mundy's goin to give us all a ride. Chub too. Soon as he makes some speech,"

Frank informed us. "First, let's go bum a ride on the merry-go-round. Hurry up, you guys."

The celebration was being held a quarter of a mile from the Thorp depot in a grove of pine trees and cottonwoods about halfway between the millrace and the river. In the grove was a space big enough for the merry-go-round. Our eyes opened up when we saw it. We only got to see it one day a year. The thick center pole stood up half as high as the tall pines surrounding it. From near the top of it, a circular canvas sloped down to cover the double seats. They swung from outriggers fitted like spokes into the hub of an axle joint in the center pole. All turned when a horse hitched there walked in a circle. This year, as usual, Mr. Haywood had brought his big bay horses to power the merry-go-round he called a swing. When one horse was pulling, the other was tied to a nearby tree feasting on a pile of hay and getting rested to take his turn on the pole. The merry-go-round hardly made a sound when turning, and the passengers sitting on the swinging red-painted boards were mostly too awed by the novelty of it to open their mouths. Sometimes only the padding of hooves on the soft dirt in the center of the ring was heard. I liked that. There were also loud noises in the grove that were glorious to me on the Fourth of July at Thorp.

The merry-go-round was loaded with twenty riders and others waited their turn. Fastened between two cottonwood trees was a plank covered with pink-figured oilcloth. Jim Smith stood behind it, busily pouring from his big pitcher into a glass and calling out:

"Here you are, here you are. Only five cents. Lemonade made in the shade, stirred by a maid with a old rusty spade."

Lemonade was nothing new to me, although I had to wonder what a rusty spade would do to it. I squeezed up to the ice cream stand where Mac stood in his white bib apron behind a table between two trees. In back of him were two tall wooden tubs painted green and covered with burlap. Small dishes were stacked on the table near a tall stack of cookie-colored cones, looking like they'd be good to eat. Mac lifted a cone off the stack and from the opened tub scooped ice cream that he piled on the bigger end of it. He handed it to a man who began at once to lick the pearly ice cream. Others followed him. It made me want one so much that I boldly stepped up, put down my nickel and pointed to the first ice cream cones I'd ever seen. Mac understood.

Supported by two-by-fours and small tree trunks and stumps in a partial clearing near the merry-go-round were twenty or so rows of planed boards, wide enough to sit on. In front, draped with red, white and blue bunting, was a bough-covered pavilion with railing around it. In the evening there would be an orchestra playing and people dancing in it. The rows of boards facing it would serve as seats and tables for those bringing picnic lunches. I was hungry and thus happy to see my mother and father getting ours ready. My mother's fried Plymouth Rock chicken that'd been fed on wheat and corn as they ran and scratched in our yard, and her potato salad made with boiled dressing were a picnic for me. I could also relish some piccalilli and delight in the fruitcake kept in a stone jar in our cellar from October until this Fourth of July.

After picnicking my mother went to join the other ladies of the Royal Neighbors, who would entertain under their drillmaster, Burt Christen, in his heavily braided and brass-buttoned blue uniform and cap. It was a good time for me to find out who was shooting off so many firecrackers back in the woods. I found Frank and Bob and Arlie just before Frank's dad arrived to suggest we all take time to go and see the entertainment about to begin. We all thought that was a good idea and ran at once to find seats facing the pavilion where the six-piece band was seated. When the Royal Neighbors began marching around, it made me uneasy seeing my mother with them. I was glad to hear the band begin playing "Columbia, the Gem of the Ocean."

The band music ended and its leader, Martin Pearson, sat down. That seemed the signal for Mr. Archie Bornel, clerk of the school board, to climb up on the pavilion, face the audience and say:

"Ladies and gentlemen: Our faithful neighbor Mrs. Lulu Turner will now lead us all in singing that grand old hymn 'America.' "

I watched Mrs. Turner, quite a buxom lady who usually sang at gatherings, walk in front of the pavilion, turn and face the audience. The band played and she sang:

> My country, 'tis of thee,
> Sweet land of liberty
>   Of thee I sing;
> Land where my fathers died,
> Land of the pilgrims' pride,
> From every mountain side
>   Let Freedom ring.
>
> My native country, thee,
> Land of the noble free,
>   Thy name I love;
> I love thy rocks and rills,
> Thy woods and templed hills;
> My heart with rapture thrills
>   Like that above.

"Come on now, everybody, sing!" Archie called out.

There was no doubt that *he* was putting all the voice he had into it.

> Let music swell the breeze,
> And ring from all the trees
>   Sweet Freedom's song:
> Let mortal tongues awake;
> Let all that breathe partake;
> Let rocks their silence break,
>   The sound prolong.
>
> Our fathers' God, to thee,
> Author of Liberty,
>   To thee we sing:
> Long may our land be bright
> With Freedom's holy light;
> Protect us by thy might,
>   Great God, our King.

At the end of the singing Archie began to speak:

"Folks, you can't beat that song anyway I know, and it was a good thing Mrs. Turner sang it. It would've been better without them dinged firecrackers popping off. But I suppose they'll keep on selling the cussed things as long as there's money in it. Be that as it is, I'd be willing to wring the neck of any whippersnapper poppin off firecrackers while our esteemed neighbor, Luther Mundy here, is speaking to us."

Mr. Mundy stood up. "Much obliged, Archie. Now neighbors, big and little, from all over the country, this Fourth of July is a glorious day you know in nearly every way I can think of. And we're glad of that. I mean, it would of been worth a lot more if Professor Klemee could have come to recite — him being used to it and so mighty interesting like he is. [Applause.] One good thing is you don't expect an old hayseed like me to be much good at this kind of business."

"You're doin good, Luther!" a man called out.

"Thank you, sir. I aim to talk to you the best I can about this glorious Fourth. Some of you might already know more about it than me, and some of you are likely too young for that. Anyhow, I'll tell you what I know about it. By the way, I see a couple of G.A.R. comrades out there today. Anybody here don't know what the meaning of G.A.R. is?"

"I ain't never heerd of it," a voice piped up from the last row.

"Is that so? Where'd you hail from, neighbor?"

"The Swauk."

"Not that. I mean before settlin on the Swauk. Where you were born."

"I come from Caroliney, mister."

"Oh, no wonder you never heard of G.A.R. standing for Grand Army of the Republic. Too bad we had to fight agin you in the Civil War."

"Oh, that's all right, mister. Somebody had to lose."

"They sure did! Now you can bet my comrades and you are glad as me that kind of war got over when it did. It took another war before it to bring us here today. It was called the War for Independence. Without it, I reckon we'd still have some king over there — what's his name . . . Edward the Fifth?— no, come to think of it, he's seventh. But it was George the Third — everybody knows he was third — who begun it. He was the last king who ever owned this 'sweet land of liberty.' And all the time he was thousands of miles from it. No wonder gentlemen such as Ben Franklin, George Washington, Tom Jefferson or Sam Adams didn't like it. Old King George wouldn't let them have any say in what taxes they had to pay him. You see, they wanted a chance such as we have to vote against any scoundrel trying to collect too much tax."

"That was danged good riddance, Luther."

"Yes, it was a good riddance all right and that's how we got to celebrate this Fourth of July clear back to 1776. That's when we took our independence from old King George of England. It was back there in the State House at Philadelphia that day. They were come there from Massachusetts to Georgia — thirteen colonies of them. Now if Professor Klemee were here he'd make this interesting. He'd relate how Tom Jefferson had wrote the Declaration of Independence and brought it to the State House for them to sign that day — provided they liked it after they read it. The professor could even tell you who all they were. Mind you now, they were asking to be hanged, in case something misfired. That old king would have hanged them in a minute. But all they said was, 'Just let him try it!' and every last one of them signed that paper giving King George notice they were *done* with him. Now comes the part that it's a sin Professor Klemee ain't here to describe. Anyway, up on top of the old State House — for twenty years — hung a big iron bell with the words writ deep in it, 'Proclaim liberty throughout all the land, unto all the inhabitants thereof.' Them sacred words come from the Book of Leviticus. The funny thing is — that bell with them words notched into it was made in England and then shipped to America where some good use was *finally* made of it."

"Say, Luther, you're good as Klemee any day!" a man shouted.

"Much obliged, Felix. Now just as I was sayin, that bell had been waiting up there ready to 'proclaim liberty' for twenty years. But all that time it couldn't do it, because there wasn't any until this July 4, 1776, when the fathers of our country collected there in the State House with their minds all made up to give us independence and liberty. The news was going to be rung out just as soon as they signed the Declaration of Independence that had taken so long to write. A boy was standing at the door watching the signing. As soon as he saw it was done, he run out and called up to the old gentleman waitin at the bell, 'Ring, ring, RING!' So ever since its ringin that day it's been called the 'Liberty Bell.' Not only that, it started Independence Day, commonly known as the Fourth of July, which we come here to celebrate. [Much applause.] Now, neighbors, I want to thank you for listenin so good. Next it would pleasure me to give every last one of you a ride in that new red Rambler. But being there's so many here I'll start out with the little folks who want to ride in it. We'll just go down the lane a piece and back. Sometime, when I meet you other folks in Thorp, I'll give you a ride. How's that?" [More applause.]

I was eager to have an automobile ride, as were Frank and Bob and Arlie, so we stood around where Mr. Mundy had to see us. First to get a ride were the four Catlin children, three girls and a boy. He drove them down toward the river about a block's distance to a place he could turn his Rambler around in. Then, after a few more trips with young passengers, our turn came, and we four boys clambered up onto the black leather-covered seats. Mr. Mundy shut the back seat door. Frank, of course, got on the front seat beside Mr. Mundy, who was wearing his Civil War cap with goggles perched on it. The Rambler had brass headlights and a brass, lantern-like fixture on each side of the dash, but no windshield. I gazed with fascination as Mr. Mundy began moving big and small levers. Then I felt a jerk, and after that the whole thing went dead. I could feel the silence as Mr. Mundy, grumbling a few words, carried a crank out to the front. But crank as he would, it changed nothing. He came back to the steering wheel and moved some levers. Then he cranked and cranked some more, but had to come back to move the little iron levers again. There was sweat on his face. He shed his cap, gauntlets and duster and laid them on the seat. George came and did some cranking, too, but nothing was changed by it. After a while, Mr. Mundy told us he would give us a ride some other time. But that big red Rambler never would go with me in it.

Chapter 10

OUR SCHOOL BELL PLEASED MISS LOVE

Our school was three blocks from home. One room of the two original rooms in the old building was divided and another built on in back before I went to school. Heat came from coal-fired stoves and water from an outside lift pump. In the first and second grade room were fifteen to twenty pupils and similar numbers in the two other grade rooms. Hardly more than half a dozen first and second year high school students were in the back room. Marriage and the inclination, often the need, to earn money limited the number who finished even two high school years. Probably the law had kept most of the others in school through the eighth grade.

My first teacher made school fairly pleasant for me, but typhoid fever laid her low the second year. I never saw her afterward. From her successor, Miss Hewit, I learned what school discipline was like. She said we'd better get used to the way Miss Love would make us behave in the higher grades. Miss Love seemed motherly to me and made me glad she and my mother were good friends in the church and in other social life. What I heard the boys in Miss Love's room say about her did not scare me.

One time she'd taken Elladine and me to see the circus parade at Ellensburg. When she saw her pupil Frank picking on me in the schoolyard she called him in and punished

him. Later that day, he wanted me to play with him. So I
had to look on the person of Miss Love at school with wonder and a sort of awe.

Miss Love had inherited enough property to make her in-
dependent of a teacher's income, but she was wrapped up in
teaching children. It seemed to me she was head of the
whole school. Her teaching methods — always approved by
parents — had to be accepted without complaint by pupils,
for Miss Love was presumed to have taught what was good
and proper. It had to be that way, or else they could get
another teacher for their precious little rascals.

No building in Thorp had been anywhere near as large
and as modern as the new school, which some who paid the
most taxes had opposed building. It adjoined the front of
the old school. To me it was like entering a new world,
going through its double, glassed front door the first time.
The plastered and painted walls of the tall, broad entrance
hall had the smell of linseed oil and turpentine. Awed by
the immensity and newness I moved on tiptoes, hoping for
some familiar sign. I knew my third grade would be in the
same room with the fourth and fifth grades. The first and
second grades would have a similar room all to themselves.
Upstairs would be the sixth, seventh and eighth grades in
one room, and four grades of high school in the other.

In the room where I saw Miss Love that first morning in
the new school, I looked for a seat and was glad to find one
with Norman Edwards near the door. But Miss Love, walking in the aisles to show pupils where to sit, soon came to me
and as though granting me a favor said, "Gordon, you may
sit with Elladine."

So of course I moved — though most reluctantly — to sit
with frilly Elladine, who always got *excellent* in deportment.

In front, almost brushing my face, were the doubled-up braids and ribbon bows of Sylvia Fields, and pressing in on me from behind were Beatrice Darby's long ribboned braids and ruffled pinafore. Across the aisle was tattletale Eunice Anderson. No boy was in safe whispering distance. Miss Love stood in front wearing a smile that did not the least bit conceal the severity reflected in her neat brown hair, smoothly rolled above her forehead. A white blouse, with ruffles on the wrists and shoulders, buttoned up in back. Most absorbing, however, was her knee-length ruffled apron of mixed-gray calico. Julius had warned me to watch out or I might get turned over it. That was the last thing I wanted Miss Love to do, as her meaningful brown eyes and the positive action of her firm hands distinctly told me. And when, with a swish of her long dark skirt, she turned to write on the blackboard, it appeared that even her apron string bow and the flounce of her blouse were giving warning. After Miss Love wrote the words *Good Morning, Children* on the blackboard, she stood in front of her desk facing us.

"It *is* a very good morning, children, when we may come to this excellent new schoolhouse. Now place your hands on your desk and fold them. Norman! Frank . . . keep them folded. Sit up straight with your feet square on the floor. Gordon! . . . We want to thank your parents and other good people who have given you so many advantages in school that they never had. Nor, of course, did you have them until today. Now, in back of you are four long, wide windows and to your left are five more. They let in plenty of daylight in a way that is good for your eyes. Even the walls above the blackboard are painted in two shades of green, restful to your eyes. And to think we have plastered walls in each room of this school. Uhh — Robert! And yes, no longer will you have to drink water from the same dipper. Instead of that, you now have sanitary fountains in the halls to drink from. Remember after this to go to the basement and not out back when you go to the toilet."

On saying that, Miss Love glanced sharply at the fifth grade row, abruptly turned and stepped behind her desk, where from a drawer she got an awesome, brown leather strap. Then, casually flapping it on her skirt, she continued talking in a very still room.

"We no longer have a stove, but those rows of pipes beneath the windows will carry steam to heat the room better than a stove could. Only this room still has double seats. Having the boys seated with the girls helps keep order in the room. The old school building will now serve as a gymnasium and assembly room where socials may also be held. Underneath it are rooms for domestic science and manual training. In the old high school room will be the stage and dressing rooms. Oh yes, the old bell has been moved into a belfry on top of this new building. We heard it from there for the first time at eight-thirty this morning. 'It is the same old bell a ringing . . . .' Those words are written on the blackboard; so we shall all sing them while I play the organ."

As Miss Love sat playing, she could easily see everyone in the room. She played and sang the song many times over; but I let the girls do the singing for me as I inaudibly moved my lips, hoping Miss Love could not detect that no sound was coming from them:

> It is the same old bell a ringing
> That our fathers used to hear,
> When they passed along the highway,
> To the old schoolhouse so dear.
> What a merry, merry way of sounding,
> What a happy ringing song,

I love to hear the school bell,
Sweetly sounding its ding-dong.
Ding-dong, ding-dong bell.

At last Miss Love stood up saying, "There. Do all of you 'love to hear' *our* 'school bell sweetly sounding'? You may raise your hands if you do. . . . Why, you all have your hands raised — I do believe."

I could see Bob had his hand up, and I knew how he cussed the sound of the bell the same as Frank, who also had his hand halfway up. The girls around me had their hands up so high that I wondered how Miss Love could see that mine was barely up at all. Whoever wrote the song must have had an uncommon penchant for learning. The bell might have been "sweetly sounding" to me, too, if it had rung when school was letting out instead of only when it was taking up. Its ring at eight-thirty meant you had half an hour to be inside the school. At nine it would ring again to make sure you were. To a boy deep in farm chores — as whoever wrote the song probably was — that bell must have been music to his ears. The law would not allow his old man to keep him doing chores after the school bell rang, giving half an hour's warning to get to school on time.

Miss Love used her organ bench for more than a seat; you bent over it lengthwise to get your lickin while she kept you from rolling off. One day she assigned me a verse from Longfellow to memorize. It began, "Let us, then, be up and doing . . . ." When she called on me to recite, I failed and so she ordered me to stay after school. Failing again meant the organ bench, and this time she did turn me over her apron. After that I could very soon recite the verse.

It was easy to give Miss Love cause to take you in hand, but one fall afternoon I gave her an unusual amount of it. Perhaps things had been getting too tame for me, so I thought of playing hooky. I knew from talk I had heard that playing hooky was the only thing to do sometime in your life. Miss Love would probably think I was home sick. To my later surprise, some missing links showed up in my assumption and so in my strategy.

Not wanting to play hooky by myself, I asked Henry Parker how he liked the idea. It suited him fine, so that cleared me of getting him to do it. My brother Pat in the first grade would naturally want to go with us, so I told him he could. A good time to take off would be as soon as we got back to school from dinner. The trick was to crawl untorn through the barbed wire fence and be hid in the willows next to the school backyard by the time the bell was ringing for the kids to line up and march in at one o'clock. Watching that activity from among the protecting willows, with the bell sounding far away from us, was even more exhilarating than I had expected it would be. But after that, it seemed that to play hooky right we had to do more than stay hid in some brush along a swampy irrigation ditch watching frogs.

"Say, Henry," I whispered, "what d'yuh say we sneak way back over there to where that water is spouting outa that flume?"

"Yeah," he said, "but in that ditch is where Normie Burnet got drowned. I'm scared of it."

"Oh, that was last week or maybe even last month," I consoled him. "I know how to swim. Come on. Nobody'll see us if we keep by them trees."

Henry and Pat waded through the yard-wide ditch after me. We had then to cross a pasture to get to any trees. The first thing I knew, Pat had stepped in some fresh cow manure. It had been Mr. Lowe's red and white cow with gallons of milk in her bag. We stopped to gaze back at the schoolhouse. It looked entirely deserted. Nobody was in

sight, except out on the road where Andy Lowman was up
on a wagonload of baled hay driving his team. I thought of
the others at their desks listening to Miss Love, and my
conscience misgave me. But I couldn't let Henry and Pat
know that, or we never would get going.

We ran as far as the cottonwood trees, only to meet
another barbed wire fence. To get through it without being
torn, two had to hold the wire up for the other. Then
Henry said he could see Mr. Lowe's mean bull eating grass
at the other end of the field. When I saw him, I secretly
prayed he wouldn't see us. But he raised his head and
walked menacingly in our direction. It was time to get out
of there! On the other side of the field was a high, wide-
board gate, so we made a beeline for it. Even Pat outran me.
We all beat the bull to the gate and hastily climbed over it.
I liked that gate.

We crawled through more barbed wire fences before
reaching the railroad. It was so hot we couldn't wait to get
to the big ditch for a drink. The rule not to drink out of
ditches didn't seem to apply when we were so thirsty. We
had another barbed wire fence to crawl through before we
got to the wide ditch, too swift and deep for us to stand in.
The bank was steep, so Henry and I held Pat by his feet
while he drank. Then it was Henry's turn, and then mine.
The water was warm and too richly flavored. I was glad no
one saw us drink it.

"What do you do playing hooky?" Pat plaintively asked.

"I know, let's go down and hike over the flume," I
exclaimed.

It took about a minute's running on the ditch bank to get
to the flume where a plank was laid down the center. Walking it was more scary than I'd expected, and I wanted to get
off. But it bothered me most seeing Pat on that narrow
plank, where he could easily trip and fall off anytime into

that awfully deep, swift water like little Normie Burnet had.
I could see the wagon road way down below us. It was bad
enough for Henry and me, to say nothing of Pat. To hear
the water thundering down from a hole in the flume made
me fervently wish I had stayed on solid ground. Even school
would be better — if Miss Love never knew we played
hooky.

I could see the kids were out in the schoolyard at recess.
Then from the belfry came the *ding-dong . . . ding-dong . . .*
telling them to march back inside. From where we were it
didn't look so bad. It even made me think I'd like to be
there. Playing hooky wasn't so good as I'd heard it was.
Anyway, it was getting time for us to be hid in the brush by
the road near the school, waiting to walk home with the kids
going by. That way, nobody'd ever know we were gone.

Going back, we wanted to stay clear of the bull, so we
followed the other side of the fence from him. We also
wanted to keep out of sight of anyone inside the schoolhouse
and hoped bending over low as we walked would do it.
That was hard to do, but better than getting caught. We
waded the ditch again and at last seemed safe among the
willows near the schoolhouse. We came to an empty pigpen
that seemed the right place to wait for school to get out. We
were so tired we didn't mind stretching out on the ground
where the pigs had left their footprints. I closed my eyes and
listened for the first shouts of the kids tearing out of school.
There was a crackling sound close behind me, then a familiar, low-pitched voice, "It seems like you boys'd rather
be in a pigpen stead of school."

It was Mr. Jones, the janitor, who also was the truant
officer. We got on our feet in a hurry and stood looking
down. I managed to say, "No, Mr. Jones, we'll stay in school
next time. Won't we, Henry?"

"Yeah, me too! This ain't no fun!"

With a smile Mr. Jones said, "Sounds like you got the right idea. Sposin you come long with me to the schoolhouse. Mebbe they won't do much to yuh this time, seein how you won't do it again."

To hear him say that sure made me feel better. But it was still a worry as we walked up the steps and into the hall, where Miss Love at her door motioned for Henry and me to enter. It was more of a worry when she told Henry and me to stay after school. The noise that followed must have been heard a long way off. That was the last time I played hooky from school.

Chapter 11

MR. NEWGATE'S STORY

On an April Saturday morning we had breakfast of sour milk pancakes made from batter kept in a gallon stone jar in back of the huge kitchen range. We put lots of butter, syrup, prune butter or honey on the pancakes and washed them down with rich Jersey milk, always kept in a pitcher on the table at mealtime. After breakfast my three brothers and I fooled around in the two little rooms back of the kitchen where we slept. On this morning when it got boring there, I decided to find out what was going on in the store. I passed through the kitchen and into the dining room, from where I could see my mother in the parlor talking to Mrs. Hahn. My mother had to have an operation and planned that Mrs. Hahn, an easygoing person about fifty years of age, would come to keep house and cook for us during the summer. With her around I could get away to play with Frank and Bob anytime.

I pushed open the door into the store and entered. I could see Jim Lane sitting over at the desk near the tall, barrel-like cast-iron stove. Jim was using the rubber end of his pencil to turn the pages of the big book in front of him. He paid no attention to me. Careful not to attract anyone else's attention, I moved cautiously behind the counters toward the front of the store and soon was behind the candy case next to the tobacco. But candy did not interest me so soon after filling up with pancake syrup. I lifted up the handle of the broad, hinged blade used to chop a plug of chewing tobacco into five cuts. The blade was thickened with remnants of moist tobacco stuck firmly to its sides. It made me turn up my nose. Chewing tobacco — no matter how I tried — made me sick.

By peering between the glass cigar case and the glass candy case, I could see Bill Nightingale behind the dry goods counter unrolling a few yards of pink-figured outing flannel. Mrs. Ricksall stood on the customer side of the counter, watching as he measured and cut it. I had seen that done many times before, so I decided to investigate the rear of the narrow store which ran — except for a shed at the back end — from the street to the alley. Tim's Place, a saloon, was on the corner across the street, parallel to our store.

I tried to move lightly, but the floor boards squeaked a little anyway. They were worn thin in places. The phone on the wall near the stove rang one long and two short. Jim got up and walked a few steps from the desk to answer.

"Hello, hello?" No answer. Jim pulled the plug from the three-six line hole and poked it into the three-eight line hole.

"Hello, hello?" But no answer there either. Better try the long-distance hole. The line in it went directly to Cle Elum, twenty miles away.

"Hello, yes, this is Orr's store. You want Mr. Orr? Hold the line. Oh, Mr. Orr, long distance wants you!"

My dad was back toward the rear of the store, weighing a scoopful of tenpenny nails for Mr. Ricksall. But he left the nails and quickly walked to the phone. Long distance was important. So important that to make sure it reached there, he put power enough into his voice that any connecting line seemed unnecessary. In recent years the means for putting electric current into a line to carry a voice a long distance had been invented, but out there in the country my dad talked as though unaware of the invention.

Near the double-windowed side door at the rear of the store, Mr. Stone, the cobbler, was seated on a low bench. Between his legs he held an iron jack with the top end stuck into a last and a shoe fitted on it. He was nailing down a half sole. Mr. Stone's gray hair was thin, but his short gray whiskers were thick. His spectacles rode on the tip of his nose. He looked up at me.

"Why ain't you in school, Chub? Oh, that's right, it's Sadiday. Better watch what you're doin. Your papa and mama got nough to worry bout as tis. Just take good keer now."

"Say, Mr. Stone, do you like electric lights?"

"Why not? Whensoever it's dark, they's the best there is. See that ol coal oil lamp hangin up yonder on the ceiling? Well, it was a blame sight better'n candles ever was. Then them pipes there hangin down come after the lamps. Burnt gas made from carbide to light em. But these here ilectrical lights beat anythin I ever seen. No tellin what's next."

There was nothing in the store to eat, except candy and gum, or maybe tobacco for a strong enough stomach. There were drugs and shoes and lace and ribbon. But I wished my dad would have kept things like bananas and pickled pigs feet. Things like that.

It was early May and the Kittitas breeze was blowing hard. My mackinaw felt good, none too thick even though the sun was bright. I eased out through our backyard gate, closed it, and put the loop of worn rope back over the ends of the pickets to keep the gate from swinging. I heard no call of my name from the house.

As I came out of our alley, I could hear shouting over at Tim's Place where already they seemed to be celebrating Saturday. Back of Tim's on the alley all was quiet around the old remodeled barn. Then I saw one of its newly-framed windows open and a man step out through it. He was the same man I had seen wearing a derby hat and carrying what looked like groceries and meat into that house on other days. A woman came to the window and, after calling him back, handed something to him. There was a mystery about the place that made people whisper. At times some fancily-dressed, laughing young women came there, whom I could guess were not wanted in the society of our village. But it didn't concern me, so I went on my way. Frank might be at his dad's blacksmith shop.

The wind blowing as hard as ever still could not carry away from me the merry high-to-low rings of the heavy hammer playing on the anvil in the shop, heard far beyond the village limits. I walked along the grassy bank of the irrigation ditch which was about three feet wide. On Railroad Street it ran next to a board sidewalk that stopped at this side street. I followed the ditch around the corner and soon was at the hitching rack across the pebbled street from the blacksmith shop. Through its big double door I could see Frank bending up and down to turn the crank of the blower that made the anthracite embers in the forge glow white-hot.

There were hundreds of worn-out horseshoes piled in a stack near the door. Early this morning Bob Turner had brought in his matched bay logging team to have them shod. One of the team was tied at the hitching rack. The other was tied inside the shop, having shoes fitted and nailed to his hooves. Frank beckoned me to come inside. His dad, wearing a heavy leather apron with divided legs, had his tongs clamped on a red-hot horseshoe, drawing it from the forge. He placed the horseshoe flat on the anvil and sprinkled some welding compound on the toe of it. Quickly with the tongs, he fitted the prongs of a red-hot calk into the holes at the toe. Holding the horseshoe again with the tongs, he gave the toe of the shoe a tremendous blow with his heavy hammer. Sparks burst up and over me like fireworks on the

Fourth of July. Frank laughed to see me jumping back too late to avoid them. He knew they were harmless.

When his dad was not watching, Frank moseyed to the back of the shop and out the side door with me on his tail. He said, "Let's go see if we kin find Bob. The local is in. Mebbe we kin hook a ride on it."

We found Bob close to the sidetrack looking for us. The local's engine was busy switching cars up around the depot. Most of its boxcars and gondolas were left standing on the track near us. We soon got to them and found an empty boxcar with its door open.

Frank commanded, "Come on, guys, let's climb on this'n. Here, Bob, put your leg up, and I'll hist you up onto it. There. Now, Chub, you hist me up while Bob pulls me. That's it. All we gotta do now is get you up here, Chub. Here, give us both a your hands. That's it. Everybody's in now. We better hide back here till the brakie goes by."

We saw the brakie go by on his way to the caboose, but by that time the train had started on its way. It kept going faster, and I got worried.

"Frank," I cried, "how we going to get off?"

"Aw, nothin to worry about, Chub. We'll ride er till we git to Bagley."

"Yeah," Bob assured me, "this local freight always stops there to git water. It's only three mile up there."

"Three mile! That's a long way off from here," I moaned.

"We'll git you back all right, Chub," Frank promised. "Don't git scared."

The freight train kept picking up speed. When we passed the Thorp depot I saw Mr. Mounts standing at the signal levers inside the bay window. I was scared he'd seen us. But Frank wasn't scared.

"Come on, you guys. Now we're outa town, we kin sit

down here and hang our feet outa the door. Get down here, Chub, in between me'n Bob."

I could see the schoolhouse a ways over and heard Bob say, "Ain't you glad this is Saturday and that ol bell sittin up there ain't ringin fur us to line up to march in that dumb schoolhouse? Left, right, left, right. Can't yuh hear ol lady Love out there? Boy, am I glad I'm gittin outa her room fur next year."

"Me too," Frank emphasized. "Even ol lady Waite ain't as bad as ol lady Love. Makin yuh sit all day with some goody girl. Poor Chub's still gotta go to her!"

"Oh, there's the gristmill and the sawmill over there," I said, changing the subject. "The light plant's there too. Look how white them waterfalls are. Below them is a good place to listen to the millrace."

"Yeah," Bob agreed. "I wonder how much farther till we come to a stop?"

"Aw, it's a long ways to Bagley. Gotta cross a big steel bridge over the river," Frank informed us.

The distance melted away as we took in the sights along the railroad and talked. Before we knew it we were looking between heavy steel beams of the bridge far down to the rushing, swollen river. Suddenly, the kind of clicking that wheels made turning over on a bridge stopped. And we were stopped! Right in the middle of the bridge! Looking ahead we could see the locomotive at the water tank.

"Criminy sakes!" Frank exploded. "Looky where we stopped! No tellin where this train'll stop again. How we goin to get off here?"

"*You* tell *us*," Bob challenged. "I ain't never stopped here on this bridge before."

"There's a plank runnin along down there," Frank said, a little hopefully. "Take hold of my hands, you guys, an hang on till I kin git my feet close to it. Gee, it's an awful narrow plank though. How'm I gonna stick onto it till this crazy train moves off'n here? Are you scared, Bob, much as me?"

"Oh no, not me!" Bob said mockingly.

Of course I was shaking with fear but managed to hang onto Frank's one hand, and Bob held his other hand until his feet reached the plank. Then Frank helped me with Bob holding on above, until I stood on the plank too. I soon got down as flat as I could get. I tried not to look down at the boiling torrent, but my eyes could no way be averted from such a dizzy, petrifying sight. Then, with a little needed help and encouragement from Frank, I stood up and helped Bob down until he stood between us. Next, I knelt down on the all-too-narrow plank and crawled a ways on it to give Bob room to lie down. All three of us lay there, hugging the plank in terror, until the train with a sudden thunderous noise moved off the bridge. We then crawled over onto the ties between the rails where it seemed safe to stand up. I didn't breathe easy till we got across the bridge to the water tank.

To recover from our fright, we sat down on a timber in the shade of the tall tank. The wind had subsided and the sun felt warm. Bob shed a gray, rough-neck sweater and Frank removed his tan duck coat buckled down the front. I took off my mackinaw. All three of us wore white duck caps that had something about paint on them. At the store my dad had given one free to each kid who asked for it.

In hardly more than a whisper, Frank said, "Look, coming down there on the track. It's Mr. Newgate."

"Yeah," Bob, who sat in the middle, whispered. "That's him. A long time ago I think he might've shot somebody. Maybe killed them."

"Aw, he don't hurt nobody," Frank scoffed. "He just

likes to look straight at you. His eyes ain't much blacker than Bob's."

I had seen Mr. Newgate in our store many times when he would say to me, "Howdy there, spindle-shanks." Then he would feel my leg and say, "No, I reckon it ain't you this time. You been stuffin again." Gently ribbing me that way always made his eyes twinkle. But now, as he left the rail-road track and came slowly walking our way, his unwavering black eyes beamed straight at us. He seemed uncertain who we were. Beneath the bill of his cap, also advertising paint, his eyes shone darker than ever. A luxuriant iron-gray beard reached down to the bib of his faded blue overalls. His gray plaid jacket had a couple of safety pins where buttons be-longed. But on a warm day neither was needed. His jacket was wide open, and his thumbs were hooked under his over-all suspenders. Mr. Newgate was lean and bent, so much taller than most men it made me look up to him, hoping to see him in good humor. Sometimes he would keep me guessing about that. Not this time though.

He stopped a few steps from us and took off his cap. Then examining it quizzically he said, "I'll be switched if this here cap ain't a dead ringer for them you boys are sportin. You goin to paint that ol water tank, mebbe?"

"No, Mr. Newgate," Frank replied, "these caps don't mean that. We was restin here."

"How bout you, Chub? What you doin all the way up here where there's nothin to eat?"

"I came up with Bob and Frank after breakfast," I replied.

"Well then, seein you're all restin, how bout me comin in?" As Mr. Newgate spoke he sat on the timber near Frank.

"Sure, Mr. Newgate, you own this more'n we do," Frank said agreeably. "How far way do you live from here?"

"Do ye know what a quarter mile is, mebbe less? That's how fur away I live, yon side a them willows."

"How long you lived there?" Bob asked.

"Well, les see. It's been a lot longer'n I care to go back to, the way it was. You boys all put together couldn't a made a gleam in even one eye by the time I come up here."

"Did you come in a covered wagon with oxen?" Frank asked.

"There weren't nothin else to come with. How'd *you* get up here? Hopped a ride on that freight what went by here, didn't you? Well, time I come up here them steel rails you rolled over wasn't dug out of the ground yet."

"Did you have much to eat, Mr. Newgate?" Bob asked.

"Yeah, much a nothin," Mr. Newgate said, nodding his head.

His elbows were propped on his knees, and his gaze was on the ground. He took a curve-stemmed pipe from one shirt pocket and a can of Velvet tobacco from the other, filled the bowl and lit it. The first wisps of fragrant smoke floating by made me wish to be in a cloud of it.

"That's right, much a nothin. There was plenty a sage-brush, but there wasn't much a it even the bulls could eat, say nothin a me and my woman." Mr. Newgate clipped his words in a deep, raspy voice.

"What did you have to eat?" I asked.

"Jack rabbits, a course. Ever eat a jack? You would've, if you was hungry as me that day. Lucky thing, though, that river there was swimmin with fish and no sneaky game warden ever gettin in sight. We was first in here and worked our fingers to the bone them years. Ever foot a them green fields up yonder was covered with leathery sagebrush. Had to clear it off without much more'n my bare hands. I dug a ditch from way up the river to water wheat and alfalfa we planted. Pretty soon we had a young orchard a apple, pear and plum trees, besides cherries and apricots. Them choke-cherries always was here. Now and again some deer'd get too close for his own good, so time our kids was bein born we had a plenty to eat. That big red wagon bridge weren't built then, but we forded the river down below goin to the tradin post where the mills was. You seen em there today. Then that cuss moved in on me up the river."

No smoke was coming from Mr. Newgate's pipe so he put a match to it while giving a sidelong stare past me back to where he had come from. Puffs of smoke leaped rapidly from his lips until, as though to catch his breath, he held the kindled pipe out in front of him. I could hardly wait for him to begin talking again.

"Ed Hadley it was. Had hisself some kind a high bindin business down there at the Burg. That's where his family stayed so's to keep away from him up here. He was that mean. Even dammed up my ditch one time in dry weather. It showed how ornery he was. He made a road through my property next to him. It was easier'n goin round. So I warned him bout it more'n once. But meetin him one day drivin on my land, he thumbed his nose at me. Next he reached under the seat and come up with a repeatin rifle. Well, bein unarmed as I were then, I quit tryin to stop him that time. But I swore that day he'd quit usin my property so's to make it his'n, or one of us'd be left in a bad fix. In them days you needed a rifle to protect your property from a skunk sech as him. That day I was back up there in the field with my team and wagon haulin bundles down below to stack. Took along my rifle, just in case. It was the day Hadley'd probably be drivin out. I knowed that. And I knowed he'd be drivin me off my property with his rifle like he done before, if I'd let him. Not that I aimed to shoot him. Just aimed to bluff him into not comin on my property like he owned it. I didn't aim to get shot by him neither."

Mr. Newgate paused to light his pipe and, half turning, gazed sharply past me to where — half a mile away — only room for the river and the railroad was left between the crowding rock walls of the mountains that farther on spread out to form the valley we boys had left that morning.

"Then it happened." Mr. Newgate spoke in a low, slow voice. "That day I was pitchin hay and sweatin in the heat and wishin I had a dipper or so a well water. Hearin a noise a comin, I straightened up to look around. It was him sure enough, skinnin his team straight down my road, same as he owned it. I figgured he'd brung his rifle, but nonetheless I left mine in the wagon so's to keep from startin a war right off. I walked up in front of his team till they stopped. Hadley yelled at me to get outa his way or else he'd put a bullet in my gizzard. I seen him reachin down for his rifle, so I hustled back to the wagon to get mine.

"By the time I got my rifle and turned round, Hadley had his'n up aimin at me. His'n never went off. Mine did. He kept on drivin the way he was goin, and I never cared no more to stop him. I wished then he'd kept off my property, though."

The fire was out in Mr. Newgate's pipe, now held in his hand and resting on his leg. He turned partly around, and I could see his gaze was on the road that went to town. His place was at this end of it. Holding steady, he began talking again.

"Next day comin outa the barn I seen this hack drivin up in front a the house. There were two men wearin black Stetsons in it. The metal on their chests was shinin so I knowed it was the sheriff with his deputy. They showed me a warrant for my arrest so there weren't nothin to do but get my coat and go with them. When they had me in the hack willin to go along, they put irons on me hand and foot. The woman and all a them were standin there and that was the hardest part of it. Weren't nothin they could do.

"That was the longest ride I ever had down to the Burg. When you're in a fix like I was in, you get to see who ain't your friends. People don't seem to reconize you when they got you tight in irons. It shows you're guilty even for defendin your own property. But that ain't nothin to what it was gettin shet up in that rat-ridden calaboose they had down there."

"How long did you have to stay there, Mr. Newgate?" Frank asked.

"Too long! It didn't make no difference, me bein innocent. Time they hauled me away from here there wasn't any big steel bridge there across that river. Time I got back here there was. You see, Hadley was a Loyal Peer — same as the prosecutor and the whole shebang of them down there. I couldn't meet no honorable lawyer. Had to hire me a low-down attorney who turned out to be a Loyal Peer wantin to help prosecute me. That's what I did: paid him to prosecute me. I oughta known better'n hirin a cussed attorney with a name like Cowslip. But when you're on the wrong side a iron bars, charged with first degree murder like I was, you don't get a great deal comin in to pick from. If it hadn't been a Loyal Peer I shot tryin to kill me, they'd a turned me loose the first day."

"Say, Mr. Newgate," Frank asked, "what were they goin to do to you for not lettin him kill you?"

"Hang me! That's what first degree murder means. Hangin. One good thing is you didn't more'n have to go outside to get that done and over with. Still and all, you can be positive I never wanted hangin. Bein in peril of it put me in a cold sweat ever last night until the jury come in and called it second degree. Before it was done they called it manslaughter. But if I'd known what that meant for me, I might a sooner had it first degree.

"See that little house through them trees? That's where Frank and Lavina lived then. He took sick after I come back, so they buried him on that little hill across the river. He testified for me. Lot a good it done. I'll tell you somethin. . . . Early one mornin, they come to see me in jail. But instead they met me comin out with irons riveted on my ankles. When they seen me, they looked like they felt most as bad as I did. And they wasn't chained to another criminal gettin transported to Seatco prison like I was. Do you know where that infernal bullpen was? No. . . . You don't learn about that in school. It's gone anyway. When it burnt down, the governor of the Territory, in his swanky office twenty miles up north, coulda heard them lice and bedbugs fryin and sizzlin.

"Startin out that mornin I never knowed where I was goin, but I knowed them irons was on so's they'd stay for an awful long ways. That blacksmith done a thorough job. I could tell that, if nothin else. So this Seatco agent was safe enough, bein with two criminals in a wagon loaded with spuds bound for The Dalles. It was so long and miserable gettin there that I swore the only way I'd come back that way was in a coffin. From The Dalles to Seatco was on a train, and that got to bein an awful long way tied up in chains. But this steely-eyed chaperon watchin us every minute didn't care what we thought a the trip. The main thing was to make sure he got us put in that hellhole known as the Territorial Prison.

"When you're travelin in chains you get looked at more'n you want. A sight of you lets the lowest kind a bum feel important as a county judge. Any man likes a pretty girl castin her eyes at him but not starin at the way he moves his feet the length of a short chain or has to lift both hands up at once to eat a sandwich. It's hell on earth, bein bound hand and foot, seein everybody goin and comin any way they want to, or bein told every step to take by some lawman you know dang well never was the man you are, any more'n the poor devil chained to you was. That might sound like crowin, but it took a man to do what I done with this land up here, and the more I live, the more I know it. Sendin me there just long enough to make a convict out a me for defendin my property didn't change me none neither."

In a concerned tone, Bob asked, "How bad was it in that place, Mr. Newgate?"

As though hesitant to tell more, Mr. Newgate lit his pipe again and puffed thoughtfully on it. His gaze was toward the nearby, fast-moving river for a few moments. Then, as his eyes shifted to the ground, he took off his cap and clapped it over his knee. His abundant, nearly-white hair was uncombed and rumpled. He said:

"The next afternoon the train stopped for maybe the hundredth time and I seen on a post it said: SEATCO. Bout that time the lawman was jerkin his hand toward the door meanin to 'get out.' A course we had to step short goin clankin outa the car, so the passengers got somethin to stare at again. The prison was close to the railroad and no steps taken to it was near short enough for me. I seen there was a coal mine lookin like it'd be a hole there they could work you in. Then I seen this wooden buildin inside a tall board fence. Without them tight irons on me, it'd taken more'n one lawman with a loaded gun to a gotten me inside a it. The train a puffin outa sight and the rain a drenchin me wouldn't a made no difference. Member, I was in the war and seen the point of a bayonet headed in my direction all of a sudden one time. But that never curdled my blood or chilled my bones like seein the barred windows on that wretched buildin with a wall around it. And the rain a pourin down. . . . It was night there. Day was here on the ranch, where the alfalfa was in bloom and ripe for makin hay — you can know it."

Mr. Newgate stood up almost as tall as the steel railroad bridge. He looked toward his ranch and slowly put his cap back on his head. His pipe was in his mouth, but no smoke came from it. Seeming in deep thought, he hooked his thumbs under his suspenders and lumbered back toward the railroad. But before reaching it, he turned and — with his ever bright and piercing eyes on us — came back and sat on the timber again.

"Boys oughta know how tis inside so they're not hankerin to get in there to find out. That big cage they was puttin me in mebbe was longer'n that bridge and four times wider. You hada climb steps to a second floor porch to get inside. Then you was steered downstairs into a cell and locked up. Sittin there a spell made you certain you never had no sech thing as a friend. No tobacco neither. They took it. Couldn't even smoke in the stinkin cell.

"After a time I got to hearin a scareful clangin and rattlin outside . . . like I was down under it . . . and it a gettin worse. You know it, a hundred a men's chained feet a rampin up a long stretch a wood steps lets out a terrible racket. There I was, locked up listenin and wonderin what's next.

"Them men was comin back inside after bein in the woods all day choppin and sawin logs. Prison stripes gets mighty thin workin out in that rain. Only drunks in black oilskins with loaded rifles could force even heavy-chained men to do it. The warden was who done it. He was a big, potbellied hunk with a black mustache. You knowed he never done a day's work. But at that place, he was the only law there was. He and some other scalawags got paid for all the work they could force you in doin for nothin. That's what I got to know about em later on.

"In a prison there might be some dangerous men. So to make sure none'd be dangerous in that one, they had enough leg irons made to torture every wretch they kept there with. That meant they even put them on a farmer like me for defendin his own property. They did it the first mornin out in the blacksmith shop. You think a blacksmith is to shoe horses? Down there his job was to hobble men. First, the irons already riveted on me had to be cut off so's I could get into a striped suit. There's a loaded rifle ready for aimin at you just in case. So I done like he said and laid down with my feet on an anvil. When that brute was done hammerin, I had fifteen pounds a iron on feelin like it was growed to my ankles.

"In no time after that I was out in the woods on the business end of a crosscut saw. The way I was sweatin and in the rain — I couldn't get any wetter. A striped suit is made so cheap it don't keep out no weather . . . so you got used to cold . . . or died. When you're wet, you go to bed wet. You can't take your pants off with them things on. Yuh can't even scratch where it itches."

"Gee, Mr. Newgate, that was a awful bad place to be," Frank said. "Couldn't you get out of there someway?"

"Well, there was a way out after a few months, as lucky it happened. Some of them poor devils was there for years, losin all the sense they ever had. I was lucky gettin out in time to keep some a mine, mebbe. It was them buildin the new penitentiary at Walla Walla that done it. Buildin a place a that kind ain't reckoned as good news for them in trouble with the law. But next to gettin back to this ranch it was the goodest news I could get. The Territory was growin fast and gettin to be a State. They had to have a bigger prison, so while they was at it they built a better one. Not good — just a whole lot better than the one we shook

our fists at the mornin we left it to get on the train for
Walla Walla.

"It took two passenger cars and a baggage car to haul
about a hundred of us there, still miserable fast in irons.
But when we was safe inside the gun-mounted wall at Walla
Walla, the blacksmith got busy cuttin the rivets and takin
them off. We were the first bunch in the new penitentiary
and probably were the last one ever made happy gettin into
it. But it wasn't no picnic very long there, either. Then one
sunny morning I got word the governor was lettin me go
home to raise what food my big family back here needed.
There yuh are, boys. That's the first time anybody ever
heard that whole story. It shows no matter how right you
are, it don't help you none if you're behind a them bars. Be
careful what you do."

When Mr. Newgate stood up now he looked to me even
taller than the bridge. He looked toward his ranch as he lit
his pipe and puffed slowly. Then he clasped his hands
behind his back and lumbered off in the direction from
which he had come.

Chapter 12

VIEW FROM THE HILLTOP

"Gee," Bob sighed. "That Mr. Newgate sure had a awful bad time. How wouldja like to been him? I'm goin to be careful what *I* do. How bout you guys?"

"Yeah, me too," I replied.

"You have to watch out you don't get in jail," Frank emphasized. "Look what all happened to him. Say, I know what we can do, though. Old John Bowles runs the gas engine to pump water from the river into this tank. He lives round here somewhere. Let's hike over there. I think that's where he lives — back of them trees."

Not far from the tank, we came to a crossing over the rails. From it a narrow road ran beside the river several hundred feet and then turned through the woods and over the towering red wagon bridge. Near the crossing was a little unpainted house.

"That's where old John lives," Frank announced. "Wonder whether he's home. I don't see nobody — just a cow in the pasture. Lucky his roan horse ain't there neither. Let's go see. Mebbe we can swipe an apple apiece. I'm starved!"

We couldn't find Mr. Bowles around the house anywhere, but in back of the house we found a door to his dugout cellar. It wasn't locked, so Frank was soon inside.

"Come on down, you guys," Frank called. "There's lots of swell yellow apples in here. Hurry up!"

Inside the cellar we took two apples apiece and got out of there in a hurry. No telling when Mr. Bowles might come home. When we got back to the road, we heard a noise coming from the direction of the train tracks. Turning, we saw Mrs. Doyle coming in her buggy. Also we saw that she knew what we'd been up to, and when she whipped up her horse, we knew it was time to scoot out of there. We took off down the road like we were being chased by the devil himself. When the road turned right to go over the bridge, we kept on up the hill through the brush. It was no use. Mrs. Doyle was on her way to Thorp and without losing any time would tell my dad and Frank's dad and everyone there all about us.

But we ignored any threat of trouble, unless it was right on top of us. So quite unworried we went on up the hill through the yellow sunflowers and the blue and pink lupines in full bloom. We tramped over daisies, blue larkspur and yellow buttercups. Before long they would be dried up, but now the hills were carpeted with their brilliant spring colors.

"Bet you never seen so many flowers as this, Chub. Not in one place anyways," Bob emphasized.

"I guess not," I answered.

We went on climbing, and when we came to an old pine tree nearly bent to the ground by the determined wind, we stopped underneath it to eat an apple apiece. There wasn't another tree anywhere in sight. But here by this one was a tiny cool spring, and we immersed our faces drinking from it. Then our apples proved that what they said about stolen fruits being the sweetest was the truth. Nothing could have tasted better than those apples.

When we got to the top of the hill we had a clear view — all new to me — down into the green valley. There was no wind. We could see the millpond next to Kendall's flour mill and Mills's sawmill and light plant. They were two miles away from us. Farther on was the Methodist church with its steeple atop the big bell. Near it was the new school-house. The old schoolhouse, where we all drank water from one tin dipper, was tacked onto the rear of the new building. The blacksmith shop, stores, saloons, the barber shop, the butcher shop, rooming houses, the post office, the Christian church, and houses on the alley were close by the school-house. The river ran along the base of the white cliff where we stood. We stayed back, for it was a hundred feet down to the river. We could have gone back down the hill and crossed on the wagon bridge and probably have gotten a ride back home on some wagon, but Frank said:

"Let's walk along the top of this hill and look for some Indian arrowheads. We can get across the river on that other railroad bridge you see way down there. It's lots of fun going this way."

The mountains to our left seemed near, with timber and snow high up on them. We were walking on top of the bluff along the river that we had sat and gazed at from the school-room many times on warm spring days. But on those days we could only dream of being where we were now.

We kept walking and looking, but we never found any Indian arrowheads that day. I knew what they looked like — pieces of flint chipped to a point. Bob and Frank had each discovered one or more on other days at other places. We did find enough white camass blooms close to the ground. We knew their bulb-like roots as Indian bread. The tops broke off when we tried pulling the roots out of the ground, but with Bob's jackknife we could dig them out. We had no water to wash them, so we had to chew and swallow more dirt than we wanted. They had a mild coal oil flavor — but we were hungry. After downing them, we were glad to have one apple apiece left to freshen up our mouths.

We sat down on a point where we could look almost straight down to the river rapids. At the same time we could look beyond the river and see our village a mile away. There were the four big cottonwood trees along the irrigation ditch that ran beside the board sidewalk in front of our house. Across the street the noon train was stopped at the depot to let passengers off and on. I could see puffs of steam and smoke rising from the locomotive smokestack as it began moving east with its three cars. It was only a local passenger train.

A block toward us from the depot was Newmans' livery stable and their home among the tall trees. The millrace ran close to the stable. Near it our swimming hole was hidden among the pines and cottonwoods. Between the millrace and the river were many wide acres of bottom land in white clover pasture, with big pine trees or cottonwoods and willows shading a spot here and there. I could see the pine stump back of home plate in the pasture where on some summer Sundays they played baseball. Nearby was the grove of trees where we celebrated the Fourth of July. Back toward the river was the pile of logs that targets were tacked onto for the Thanksgiving and Christmas turkey shoots. Lots of bullets were buried in those logs. Sometimes we dug them out with a knife. We heard a faraway train whistle. Frank said:

"That's a Milwaukee train miles from here. It's on the crossin goin over Ames's road now. See the flume there? You 'kin even see from here how it leaks. Look back this way. It looks like my dad comin out of his shop."

His blacksmith shop was on the back street near the Christian church. On the front street were three saddle horses and two teams with rigs at the hitching racks near our store.

Bob said, "I wonder who that is haulin baled hay? Chub, I bet your dad is out there weighin it."

I wondered whether they had missed me, but as it was dinnertime there could be little doubt they had. I looked to the mountains beyond Thorp and saw snow that we couldn't see from the bottom of the narrow valley. To our left we could see smoke rising from the roundhouse at Ellensburg. It was eight miles away in the wide part of the valley. But today the broad moan of its noon whistle, unopposed by any wind, came all the way to give us company. As its deep voice turned silent again, it left a loneliness for a moment, even among so many flowers atop the hill. Happily we were not far from where we could climb down and get back home over the lower railroad bridge, and we hurried to do it.

Chapter 13

IT'S DECIDED

By the time we got down off the hill we were so tired, hot, hungry and thirsty that we couldn't get home fast enough — no matter what happened when we got there. Wondering about that we all grew pretty silent. Even Frank's cocksureness seemed to wilt. When we got near home, I took a roundabout way so I would come as I'd gone, through the backyard gate — unnoticed if possible. Pat and Mike, my younger brothers, greeted me. Mike ran into the house to tell what he thought was the good news. Pat stayed to tell me the bad news.

"Hey, Chub, we ate baked beans and had some apple pie Mama made. Where'd yuh go? Mama's mad cause you run away. So is Papa."

"What'd they say?"

Pat shook his head, saying, "Mama was in there with Miss Love for a long time. Chas is looking for you, besides."

"Do they know where I was?"

Pat shook his head.

"You won't tell em?"

Pat shook his head again.

"We hooked a ride on the local. Me'n Frank and Bob did and went clear to Bagley," I bragged.

"What's up there?" Pat whispered.

"Oh . . . a great big water tank and a bridge higher'n a house. It's awful scary. We swiped some apples," I bragged again. "Don't you run off up there with Mike. You're too little!"

"Mike don't even go to school," Pat reminded me.

I knew I had better get inside. So, steeling myself for the worst, I casually walked into the house. I saw my mother and Miss Love sitting in the parlor. Their rocking chairs were still.

My mother commanded, "Young man, you get yourself in here onto that chair."

I got in the chair facing her. Miss Love sat beside me. I wished my dad was the one to settle with, but on Saturday afternoons he had more than he could do in the store.

"Now where have you been all day?" my mother demanded.

"I went with Bob and Frank over to the woods back of Newman's, and we got lost," I lied stupidly. Unknown to me, Miss Love had seen us climbing into the boxcar.

"Where is your coat you had on this morning?"

With a sinking feeling, I remembered that I'd not had my coat on since the wind quit blowing back at the water tank.

"It's back there somewhere, probably in the yard."

"Then you go find it in the yard and bring it here."

I did not move.

"How did you tear that hole in your overalls?"

I knew I had torn it climbing up into the boxcar, but then had paid no attention to it. "It got caught on a nail when we got lost."

"Oh, are there nails sticking out back there in those woods?"

I nodded my head without looking up.

"What have you had to eat today?"

"Some apples."

"Apples! Where did you get them?"

"Frank's dad gave us some." I looked at Miss Love who was shaking her head and compressing her lips. Then I looked down again.

"Gordon, how can you sit there and tell your teacher and your mother such stories? What do you suppose Miss Love will think ought to be done with you, after hearing how you story?"

"I don't know."

"Well you had better know, and you had better tell us the truth right now. How did you tear your overalls?"

"Climbing in a boxcar." (I guessed she knew anyway.)

"Oh, and why did you climb into a boxcar when you have been strictly forbidden to?"

"Frank wanted me to."

"Where did you go in a boxcar?"

"To Bagley."

"To Bagley! What did you do there?"

"Got some apples."

"Where did you get apples up there?"

"Mr. Bowles's cellar."

"When he was not home?"

"Uh, huh."

"Oh my, Myra!" (Hardly anyone else in the whole neighborhood except my mother called Miss Love by her first name.) "I don't know what I can do with him, and I don't know what I would have done without your being here today. You are a friend indeed. His father will just say, 'Boys will be boys,' but you are Gordon's schoolteacher. I know you are concerned about him, so what do you think ought to be done?"

As a consequence of having had poor health for several months, my mother was in a weakened condition. The doctor, believing that her condition was due to a "floating kidney," recommended that she have surgery to tie it back in place. Surgery then was done without the benefit of anything like a modern hospital, blood transfusions, easy anesthetics, miracle drugs, or much knowledge of antisepsis. In my mother's case, there would have to be many months of convalescence after she had the operation.

My mother, when in good health, had needed no help to manage her boys. That was one reason why Miss Love had so much respect for her and why she now sympathized with her, knowing how much my mother wished she could take the action with me that she would normally take.

"Any small boy may get into mischief," my mother continued, "but Gordon slipped away this morning when he knew he was not to leave this place without permission. He has been told and told to never get on one of those freight trains or even to go near them. It is so easy to lose a leg or even be killed in doing just what he did. For a small boy the danger is more than I dare to think of. I cannot bear the thought that he may be running off with Robert and Frank while I am away, as he did today." My mother kept shaking her head. "What can be done with him?"

She looked at Miss Love who gestured with her hands as though she were at a loss, too. But when faced with such a problem, Miss Love did not stay at a loss long.

"If Gordon were in my care today, I know what would be done," she said. "But since he is not, I do not feel that anything I could do would help to cure him of running off the way he does. I do think he should be taught not to run away with older boys like Frank and Robert. But since you will have to be in bed for some time, Mary, I see no hope of his getting the care he needs at home this summer. At best we might trust he would not get into serious trouble."

"Yes, Myra, I hate to think of it."

"As you know, Mary, it's like a miracle that he got back home safely today."

"Oh yes, I know, Myra. But what would you suggest I do?"

"Well, I have been thinking for some time that I could arrange to take care of Gordon this summer, if it would help you."

"For mercy's sake! Of course it would help me. But I don't see how we could let him go. And it would be too much of a burden on you. Do you mean you would want to take care of him in Tacoma?"

"Indeed, I would. I am used to having a little boy with me during summer vacation."

Not wanting to believe my ears, I turned to look up at Miss Love. She looked at me with a warm reassuring smile.

"Well, I know how good you are with children. Let us get Mr. Orr in here and find out what he thinks. Gordon, you step into the store and tell your father I want to see him," my mother directed. "Come straight back."

I found Papa at his stand-up desk beside the safe in the store. He scowled down at me.

"Where've you been all day, Gordon?"

"No place. Mama wants to know if I can go with Miss Love to where she lives."

"Oh? Is that so? What if I say you can?" He looked at me with one eye partly closed.

"I don't care." No use of me caring, the way things are, I thought.

I followed Papa and soon was back on the chair in the parlor.

"How-d'ye-do, Miss Love? Bet you're looking ahead to getting out of that schoolroom this summer."

"Well, Mr. Orr, I always enjoy my schoolwork, but summer *is* a good time."

"Mary, what does Gordon mean, asking me whether he can go with Miss Love to where she lives?"

"He means, Fred, that he heard Miss Love offer to take care of him in Tacoma this summer. It seems that she thinks he needs the care she can give him there, while I am getting over my operation. Am I right in saying that, Myra?"

"Yes, Mary, that *is* the way I feel about Gordon. Every time I see him in school, it makes me want to do more for him. If only he were not so fond of running with those older boys and instead played at home with his brothers, I would not need to be so worried about him."

"Myra, I'm so pleased that you take such an interest in Gordon, especially when we seem to be in need of you. I wouldn't like at all having him away this summer, but knowing he would not be near those freight trains or that swift river would be a great comfort to me. What do you think, Fred?"

"Oh . . . I guess it might be a good thing for Gordon, but I doubt it'd be much of a vacation for Miss Love. I remember when we talked about it being a good thing for him, we didn't hardly think she'd want to tackle it. But he'd have to want to go, or she wouldn't want him — that's sure!"

"Fred, there's no question about his wanting to go on any kind of a trip, and most of all, on one to a big city. Gordon, if Miss Love would take you to Tacoma with her, would you be happy there and behave?"

I nodded several times, but did not speak. I didn't want to seem too happy with Miss Love's plan, though I knew it would be put into effect no matter what. I saw the door into the store swing in enough for Bill's head to appear in the opening.

"Mr. Orr, will you come in here?" he called. Papa stood up, excused himself to Miss Love and hurried into the store. Then Mama stood up and, saying she would return in a moment, disappeared into the store after him.

Miss Love turned a little, looked out the window and said, "Gordon, where did you leave your jacket?"

"Up at Bagley, I guess." (There was no use lying to her.)

"Whom did you see up there?"

"Mr. Newgate. He talked to us and told us lots of things."

"Whom else?"

"Oh . . . Mrs. Doyle."

"Did she see you stealing those apples?"

"Maybe . . . I guess so."

"Gordon, you and those other boys ought to be punished for that! In Tacoma you will not want to be in mischief of that kind. You will like to stay home in a great big stone house with Aunt Luella and Mr. Jim. She is a fine cook and does enjoy cooking for little boys. Mr. Jim drives two beautiful chestnut horses whose names are Duke and Queen. They will take us to church and to visit friends. Mr. Jim was a cowboy pioneer and he knows lots of stories — oh — now your mother is coming. Yes, Mary?"

"Well, Myra, Mr. Orr and I agree it would be well for you to have Gordon this summer — if you want him."

"Yes, Mary, I would like very much to have him all summer long."

"I'm glad. Of course, we would pay you," Mama assured Miss Love.

"I would let you pay for his train fare, but I would accept no other pay."

"What would we do without you, Myra?"

"I should not want you to do without me, nor do I want to do without you, Mary. For while I like to think Gordon would be helped by being with me this summer, I would also be helped by him. I think we need each other. Need has to be mutual, you know. Otherwise it is never supplied."

"What do you mean, Myra?"

"Well, when I see children who need me, it makes me feel need for them. I want to care for them, teach them and love them. I have never had children of my own, so I console myself remembering that old saying: 'They who educate children well are more to be honored than they who produce them.' At least, I like to think educators deserve some honor."

"I am sure that you are honored for the way you have educated children, Myra."

"Yes, but there is a kinship between a child and a parent that a mere teacher must do without. On the other hand, I have known teacher and child relationships as beautiful as anything could be."

"You may yet have a child of your own, Myra."

Beaming all over, Miss Love replied, "Mary, you say such nice things to me. You make me almost forget to tell you the good news that Gordon will have Elladine as a little playmate this summer. She is going to stay with me, too."

Upon hearing those shocking words, I wanted to shrink farther down into my chair, but I thought it better not to call attention to myself at the moment.

"That may be exactly what Gordon needs!" my mother exclaimed. "He has simply been with boys like Frank altogether too much. Have you ever heard the way that boy swears?"

"Yes, I have," Miss Love said, nodding emphatically, "and if I ever heard him swear like that at school, I should wash his mouth out with a good, strong lye soap. But Gordon will not be with a child having any bad habits of that kind when he is in my care. For some time as you know, Mary, I have had Gordon and Elladine together in a double seat. They look like brother and sister, and I like them sitting together. I could prepare Gordon for advancement into Elladine's grade."

"I would leave that to you, Myra."

"Mary, you know that Elladine is my kin, and I live in the same house with her. But there shall never be a particle of difference in my treatment of her and Gordon. Her parents have more than they can do, and they are glad to have me take care of her in the summer. I love to do it anyway. And Elladine always likes being with me, even though I am as strict as I can be with her. Children may complain about restrictions, but they are happier when they know exactly what they may do. It is being unfair or neglecting them that does harm. You know that better than I do, Mary."

Miss Love and my mother stood up as my mother said, "Of course I know you will be with Gordon the same as you would be with your own, Myra. And I know he will have the best care any boy could have."

"Thank you, Mary. I am so happy that you and Mr. Orr are letting Gordon go with me. He shall certainly get lots of attention and be loved by all of us. My cousin Luella will be the one to spoil him, that is, as much as I will allow her to." Miss Love smiled her happiest. "I think I shall be going now. Be a good boy, Gordon. There are still three more weeks of school, so I shall be looking for you Monday morning at nine. As soon as our school term is over, we shall be having a fine time in Tacoma. Just you wait and see. Now you can tell the other children all about it."

"My, won't they be envious?" my mother added as she looked at me with a smile.

I felt a welcome sense of relief. Minutes before, I had feared some punishment severe enough to discourage me from taking part in any more escapades with Bob and Frank. So I had to feel a little gratitude toward Miss Love for having recommended what seemed like an easier pill at the moment for me to swallow. The time for me to go away with her was a long way off, I thought. By that time, if I did not want to go, I would find some way out of it. Like telling my parents that when I got away from them, I wouldn't do what Miss Love told me to. Then she wouldn't want me and they wouldn't let me go.

As Miss Love and my mother stood at the door, I noticed that my mother was half a head taller than Miss Love. But Miss Love was somewhat rounder and broader than my mother. Both had their dark hair cleanly combed and done up high, with Miss Love's looking more compact. I wondered how they could be so different in size and still have hair and eyes so alike. I had noticed, as she sat behind her desk, that Miss Love looked a little like my mother. It made me feel a kinship to Miss Love and at the same time fear there might be one.

Chapter 14

THE SWIMMING HOLE

The millrace rippled and sparkled as it poured through the narrow, brush-lined channel, then spread out into a clear, nearly motionless pool that was our swimming hole. It shallowed out to a muddy beach on one side and deepened to about three feet along the smooth, white-clovered bank on the other side. The highest point of the bank, two feet above the water, was the diving spot. All was surrounded and enclosed by clumps of willow, chokecherry and serviceberry bushes, bordering the tall cottonwoods and pines. We thought no swimming hole ever was more cozy or better hidden from the view of unwelcome girls and adults, and we liked to imagine the path to it from the rickety wooden bridge was a secret way known only to us.

Later in the summer, we would probably not hike off to the swimming hole until afternoon, but this was a perfect Saturday morning in May. And nature stirring in me and several other Thorp boys had somehow guided us to the very same street corner where we were now deciding on a course of action. It could only take us to the swimming hole, for the sun was already urging us to shed our clothes.

As we ran off to initiate the swimming season, Joe was in the lead, followed by Arlie and me. Bob and Frank and Harold (known as Cash) were slightly delayed by Cash taking time to tease Mildred and Eunice who were watching us from their yard. We climbed over the wagon gate and crossed the millrace bridge, then followed the almost invisible trail winding through the bushes and small trees until one by one we emerged onto the green bank of our swimming hole. A patch of fine river sand stretched out along the edge of the bushes. It would be just right for us to wallow in, soaking up its warmth and dryness after our first plunge into the pool's cold depths that the sun's warm rays would not reach until July.

We listened to a woodpecker sounding deep in the woods as he drilled into an old dead cottonwood. A rainbow trout leaped up to catch a darting fly, and the widening rings of wavelets slightly ruffled the glassy surface of the pool as though it were charged with electricity. A chipmunk chirped merrily as he scampered up his pine tree. It was good to be a small boy on a warm sunny day in May with a share in the old swimming hole.

Our shoes slipped off easily. Our overalls fell unsuspended to the ground. Last of all, our shirts were hastily pulled up over our heads. Our pale skin had been nine months hidden from the sun. But soon now, reddening from the sun would begin to show on us. Dangling our feet over the bank, we took the first shock of the water recently melted from the snow plainly visible on the nearby mountains. But even ice water would not stay us from opening our swimming season on a day like this. After one brave and brief ducking and a few timid splashes, we all hurried to get back where we could wallow in the sun-warmed sand. Our teeth fairly chattered. I noticed how goose pimpled Frank was on the back of his legs and bottom as, lying on his belly, he burrowed in like the rest of us. But it was not long until the warm sand enfolding us below and the sun pouring over us from above had dissolved all goose pimples and made our skin tingle.

Frank whispered to me, "Looky, Joe's got a pack of cigs he's bringin."

Sure enough, Joe had gotten a pack of cork-tipped cigarettes out of his pocket and now had a match and was cockily lighting one. This brought us right up out of our holes in the sand as we hoped to get a puff or two. We knew the smoke would sting our noses and make us dizzy, but we wanted to seem as tough as Joe.

"All right," Joe said, "take one little drag. Here, Chub, you can have the first one."

Trying to hold the cigarette as much like a poolroom dandy as I knew how, I took one drag long enough for three. It started me spitting and coughing. I staggered as I hurried back to my warm bed of sand, and soon the others were back in theirs, too. All except Joe, who stood there naked as a plucked duck, his feet wide apart and one hand to his hip. The burning cigarette nimbly held between his thumb and finger was daintily inserted into his pursed mouth. Closing his eyes and drawing the smoke in deeply, he blew it straight up over his nose or straight out to form a ring. It didn't faze him in the least, or at any rate he made us think it was a delight to him. The short burning stub was then thrown into the pool, and it floated away and under the overhanging brush, soon to be tumbling over the ripples carrying it down to the river.

Arlie Brown was a natural-born entertainer, and he couldn't wait to get into some act.

"I seen some frogs back there in that pond," he said, pointing downstream. "Wait while I get me one, and we'll have some fun with him."

Arlie started off into the brush in spite of the stickers attacking his bare skin from head to foot. He soon returned holding a small frog. But he could not make it perform, so he tossed it into the deep pool where its weak struggles could not save it from floating away to the river, perhaps becoming the victim of a mink living along the bank.

"Hey, Arlie," I called. "Remember the time we had a frog in Sunday school and put it in Beulah Smith's lap? Boy! Didn't she jump and yell?" I had to laugh. "Talk about funny! Ol lady Love made you pick up the frog and took you outside, holding your ear with you holding the frog by one foot."

"Yah," Arlie grunted, "next day at school she had to give me a lickin."

"Yeah, that's the trouble," I put in. "Having her for a Sunday school teacher, too, is like you're in school every day."

Joe said, "What do you think me and Chub and Bob did last night? We hid there behind that pile of boards by the Splawns. You know how mad Grandma gets if you tease them granddaughters of hers. Last night they were in bed when we hid there. Chub threw a rock up on the roof, and you could hear it click-clackin down the shingles. I threw another one, and right away we could see Grandpa headin out and Grandma was yellin, 'Catch them little villyans! Catch em! Bring em here!' It was pretty dark where we were, and we like to've never stopped runnin until we got clear around in front of Chub's house. We'd lost Grandpa, but Chub figured he'd better get inside, so we went on home, too. It's more fun when it's kind of dark that way. I hope we do that again right away. What d'ya say, guys? Let's get dressed and git over to old Mr. Ruth's. Boy, does he get mad when you call him 'beerbelly'! Ha ha, he couldn't catch a flea!" Joe laughed.

Inspired by that idea, we got dressed in a jiffy and ran back through the woods and over the bridge looking for new excitement. All at once Bob, who was in the lead, called back to me, "Hey, Chub, I see your pop comin."

Yes, it was my pa. After speaking cheerfully to my friends, he spoke to me.

"Gordon, you were supposed to be at home. Miss Love is there waiting now to take you to Ellensburg for the day."

That reminded me of the talk there had been of my going away with her for the summer. I would no more have thought of objecting than I would have tried to stay away from her school. Also, for some strange reason, it seemed to please me to be chosen even by Miss Love, though it wasn't something I could brag about to the boys. Far from it. They'd have shuddered to think of spending any vacation with Miss Love very near.

Chapter 15

A KIND OF FAME

As soon as we were home Papa sent me into the parlor where I found Miss Love with Mama. The scolding didn't amount to much and Miss Love concealed any disapproval she may have felt over being kept waiting during my absence without leave. Mama, I thought, had scolded me partly in deference to Miss Love and, now done with that, said:

"Gordon's hair has gotten so long, but it has been let go mainly because we don't care to have that Mr. Carrico cut it. He swears so, even at children. But when you have Gordon in town today, perhaps you would like to get his hair cut shorter."

"But, Mary, I like it in its natural length. In the city you will find that many boys of Gordon's age have never had their hair cut either."

"That may be, Myra, but isn't his hair going to be too much trouble for you, long as it is?"

"Not at all. He has such abundant, wavy hair it will be a pleasure to take care of. Luella will be taken with it, too."

"Very well, Myra, we will leave it up to you."

Miss Love was going to trade in Ellensburg, so much to my dismay I had to get dressed in my Sunday clothes to go with her. We rode on the noon train eight miles and then walked several blocks to the stores. We went into the ice cream parlor and Miss Love ordered a banana special for me — the first one I ever had. Nothing ever pleased my taste more.

Near the ice cream parlor, behind dazzling big plate glass windows, I saw dresses, suits and hats on figures that looked like people, but Miss Love said they were made of plaster. She told me to stay close by while she looked inside the store for a few minutes. With black purse clasped in one hand and white handkerchief trailing from the other, she stepped firmly through the big front door and out of my sight.

For the first time then it clearly dawned on me what going away with Miss Love would mean. But I'd learn to get around her someway. In school she could not be fooled ("eyes in the back of her head," we would say), but now, well, maybe she would look the other way and quit being such a pesterous old schoolmarm. Arlie Brown said Miss Love was like a fat fussy old hen in her long flounced skirt and ruffled blouse. And she did hover over you like one. I wondered how I could stand a whole summer with her and then the teasing it was sure to bring. Still, going away with her would give me a kind of fame the other boys might envy, so I'd better go along and try to make the most of it. I would find some way to brag about it later.

We had passed a tall, ornate iron structure with a trough full of water circling it. Now I could see two horses, one bay and one black, that had their noses in the trough. They were more than a block away from me. Coming down the middle of the street toward me was a man pushing a cart-like rig with a barrel slung between what looked like two small buggy wheels with wood spokes and iron tires. When near me the man stopped and took a coarse push broom and a scoop shovel from the cart, swept up something and dumped it into the barrel. He looked so much like our drayman Mr. Splawn that it seemed I knew him, and was so anxious to watch him work I began tagging after him. That diversion suddenly ended when much to my annoyance Miss Love appeared and impatiently took my hand.

"Gordon! I expected you to stay near me. Now you come along. I want to buy a few things for you. Pick up your feet please."

Inside the store we came to a counter quite covered with fancy-looking blouses, stockings and hose supporters. A neatly groomed lady stood behind it. I couldn't see any need of being there but Miss Love did and told me to turn around and stand still.

"I want to see how this fits you," she said. I felt something being held to my shoulders, then something else and after that the lady handed Miss Love a package.

"Turn around here, Gordon, and get this Windsor tie on. You have to look nice when we go to visit Mrs. Peabody." I turned and saw in Miss Love's hand a length of wide, pale blue silk ribbon. She quickly wrapped it round my neck and tied a bow flaring enough to hide my chin, and my ears, too, it felt like. I wanted to rip it off but in front of Miss Love did not seem the right place to do that. She picked up a package, took my hand and walked out the door.

"This is the way to Mrs. Peabody's house," she said. "Mrs. Peabody has been a primary teacher and has two girls a few years older than you are. Mr. Peabody is an engineer on the Northern Pacific and is often away from home. We can only stay at her house for a short time, so please see how good you can be there."

After walking several blocks, Miss Love turned at the gate of an unpainted picket fence. A lady was inside the fence picking flowers and adding to a bunch already in her hand. She greeted Miss Love warmly and, without being introduced, spoke to me:

"I can tell your name is Gordon, as Miss Love has told me all about you, even described your hair and freckles. She is looking forward to having you with her in Tacoma this summer. Are you glad?"

"Yes, ma'am," I replied, with tongue in cheek.

"Come in the house, where we can sit and visit. Dorothy and Mildred are visiting friends at Brunson's farm today."

"Yes, Emma, but I can only stay a short time, as we must be on the train to Thorp in less than an hour. Gordon, you may either come in the house with us or play in the yard until we go. May he use that swing, Emma?"

"Of course, and there is a wagon and other things for him to play with here."

I went and sat in the swing planning to sneak off as soon as the ladies were in the house out of sight. Miss Love looked pleased to have me swinging. But across the street was a buggy that attracted me. It looked like ours at home. When I thought no one was watching from the house, I stopped swinging and in no time at all was through the gate and to the buggy. By the time I got up into the back end of it and was about to climb over onto the seat, I heard thudding of a horse's hooves coming near. Soon a white, pink-eyed horse galloped by with a boy my size riding him. At the command "Whoa Pink!" the horse half-slid to a stop, wheeled round and, urged by two bare feet thumping his ribs, trotted back toward me. The next thing I knew, his nose was into the back end of the buggy and nearly touching me. It was a surprising encounter that put me ill at ease. I looked at the rider. Both knees of his worn blue overalls had holes. A fringe of brown hair straggled beneath the wide drooping rim of his frayed straw hat. A soiled rag was wrapped round his big toe. I had gone barefoot every chance I got but not nearly enough to get my feet so caked with dirt as his were.

"What's your name? Is it Red?"

"No. Chub."

Suddenly a barking Irish setter dog bounded from behind the nearest house and began snapping at Pink's heels.

Pink jerked his head away, reared once and bolted off down the street. It looked for sure like the rider would fly off into the air, but his legs clung to Pink's ribs like they were grown there. He jerked Pink to a stop, turned him round and trotted him toward me again. They pulled up close to the end of the buggy as a lady called the dog back into his yard.

"Say, Chub, where d'yuh live?"

"Thorp."

"What's there to do in that dinky place? Gotta horse?"

"Yeah, we got Happy to ride."

"Sounds pretty tame. Pink here's a wild cayuse. Wanta try ridin him?"

"Sure. I guess so. . . ."

"Wait till I get him turned round here so's you kin hop on ahind me. He's lible to get kinda frisky ridin double. Hope that big bow you got on don't scare him. There, you kin make it."

My leg was halfway over Pink when from across the street came:

"Gorduuunn! Do not get on that horse!"

But it was too late for me to pull back. There was no saddle for my hands to grab so when Pink decided to rid himself of the extra load and took off on a twisting run, my arms were wrapped tight around my friend in front of me. Even though his legs were quite grown to Pink's ribs, my sudden shift to the left-rear and downward proved too much. When I hit the ground he landed safe on top of me. That was all I knew then. Afterward from Miss Love I learned that this is what took place during the next several minutes:

Mrs. Peabody and Miss Love who were already into the yard rushed out to the street. Miss Love exclaimed:

"Look! He is not moving at all! Oh, this is terrible! What can we do?"

"I'll go telephone Dr. Granahan," Mrs. Peabody decided. She rushed back into the house.

Miss Love could only kneel beside me and pray while hoping the doctor would come in a hurry. His office was not far away. Then it seemed to Miss Love her prayers were being answered when she saw my eyes open.

Hazily, I saw Miss Love bent over me and Mrs. Peabody standing near. Nothing seemed real. Then the doctor appeared, as if coming down out of a cloud. He felt all over my head and helped me to sit up. It was like I was dreaming to hear him say:

"He's been stunned some. Nothing seems to be broken. Keep him in bed today, with nothing more to eat. Then give him some mush for breakfast. He should be over this by then."

"Thank you, Doctor," Miss Love said. "Your coming here has been a great help. Send your bill to Miss Myra Love, Thorp, please. Good-bye."

In a consoling voice, Mrs. Peabody said, "Don't worry, Myra. We have room for you to stay tonight. We will have a good visit. Telephone his parents he's here."

"Yes, of course. You are very kind, Emma. But just look at this. He is in some tar, and has it all over his blouse and pants. Oh dear! What shall we do?"

"Well, Myra, we'll have to do the best we can. Let's get him up and into bed like the doctor said. Those clothes are a mess, aren't they?"

"They most certainly are and he shall have to wear whatever we have for him."

Mrs. Peabody and Miss Love helped me onto my feet and, still half stunned, I walked between them into the house. There Mrs. Peabody said, "We'd better get these tarred things off of him and put them on the back porch."

I heard Miss Love exclaim, "Now look at this — he has no underwear on! The little rascal left it off unknown to his mother and me."

"Oh, don't worry, Myra. Wait just a minute, I'll get a nightgown he can wear."

I saw I was in a bed much wider, whiter and smoother than my bed at home. Nothing seemed real. In the other room there were voices mingled with the humming and clicking of a sewing machine. A voice said, "Won't he be surprised to see what we have for him to wear to church in the morning?" That sounded like Mrs. Peabody, I thought.

Then it looked like Miss Love was coming in so I knew to shut my eyes. Soon a hand grazed my forehead and a voice breathed:

"What a blessing it is to have him asleep. He did not seem fully over being stunned, even after we brought him into the house. A good long sleep is what he needs. This is the first time I have put him to bed as it will be done every evening this summer, I expect. He is all right now — but just the same I am going to ask Emma to come in here."

Again a hand grazed my forehead but it was not as warm and soft as the other had been so I guessed it was Mrs. Peabody. "He seems perfectly all right to me, Myra, sleeping like a baby. Just don't worry about him. He'll wake up in the morning as good as ever."

"I surely hope so, Emma. How can I ever repay you for this?"

On hearing that, I opened one eye enough to see both ladies tiptoeing out of the room.

Miss Love stood beside my bed when I opened my eyes. "Did I fall off a white horse yesterday?" I asked her.

"Yes, you did, Gordon, and you were naughty to get on it. We were frightened half to death. Your clothes were ruined with tar that fortunately did not get on your skin or I would have had to scrub it off. Come out here now and get washed before breakfast."

Before the washing was done I knew how foolish I had been to get on any horse. But at last, still dressed in a nightgown, I sat eating a bowl of oatmeal with cream and sugar. I asked for more but Miss Love said no, that it was time to get ready for church. Anything would be better, I thought, than wearing the kind of nightgown Mrs. Peabody had loaned me.

But then she brought out underwear and knee-length, straight pants made of some fancy stuff for me to wear. The wide-collared blouse and too long and too wide tie Miss Love had bought were even worse. Just because I had landed on that patch of tar I'd have to go to church dressed up like some clown.

At last it was time to get on the train to Thorp, but I knew I'd hate to get off there dressed the way I was. Clement Holbeck, a Thorp boy several years older than me, sat at the front of the car. Miss Love let me go up there to get a drink of water so I sat with him. We were so near Thorp she didn't interfere.

"What's all that junk you got on your shirt, Chub? And what a tie!"

"Yeah, I'll take it off and ditch it under this seat," I promised.

"Say, Chub, I got a good knife. Want me to trim your shirt so they won't throw rotten eggs at you in Thorp?"

"Sure, go ahead."

Clement worked fast, as Thorp got nearer. When he was through, there were no more ruffles on me and it was safe to get off the train.

Chapter 16

THE BELL KEPT SILENT

School had let out on Monday of the last week before summer vacation. That I would not be spending the summer with my friends in fun hardly occurred to me. At least not as, with three of them, I ran on winged feet the minute Miss Love dismissed us at the front door. By previous agreement, we were headed for the patch of willows at the lower side of the schoolyard. One good thing about that: it was taking us in the direction of home. As always, Joe could outrun all of us, and this time I was able to keep ahead of Bob and Frank. We knew Miss Love would be watching. But soon we were well-hidden among the willows, feeling free as the red-winged blackbirds nesting among the cattails beyond the schoolyard fence. We paused to catch our breath and make further plans.

"Say, you guys," I said, "let's go see if there's any pigs in that pen where I was hid the day I played hooky. It's back over there." I wanted to be sure they knew I'd played hooky once.

"Yeah, Chub," Bob said, as though he thought it funny. "You mean where Mr. Jones came and took you up to Miss Love? I thought you said you'd never go there again. But I'm game to go, if you are. Are you game, Joe?" Then Bob whispered to me, "He's got some more cigarettes."

"Yeah, I'm game as the next one. Let's go. But we got lots of pigs at home." Joe sounded disdainful.

Frank, as usual, was game for anything, so I led the way

and soon we were half over a wide board fence and could see a long pig trough on the other side of it. But there were no pigs to see that day either.

"Let's get in there," Frank called out.

There was a low, peak-roofed house on one side with an opening for the pigs into the darkness of it. Joe had to go right over and lean down to look inside. Suddenly there was an uproar of grunts and squeals, and a big black sow with bared teeth, followed by a bunch of little pigs, rushed out at Joe. He got to the fence and over it before the sow could bite him. That gave us enough time to also get back on the safer side. We sat down, glad to have our backs against the outside of the fence. The pigs went on about their business, which at that time meant a lot of noisy sucking that made us turn around to silently watch. When it was over, it was time for the pigs to nap and for us to think up something else to do.

"I'm goin to take a smoke," Joe said. "What about you guys?"

"Yeah, what about it?" Bob replied. "You wanta give us a drag or two offa yours, Joe?"

"Sure thing!" Joe said as he struck a match to light the cigarette he had already stuck between his lips. "This is a Murad from Turkey. It don't even make you sick at all. Here, try it, Chub."

Eagerly, I took the cork tip between my lips and cautiously puffed. I knew enough not to inhale the smoke the way Joe wanted me to. He said inhaling was the only way to get a kick out of it. But I was satisfied to puff it right out, and I knew there would be trouble if it was learned at home I even did that.

"Say, guys, do you know where Chub is going when school gets out?" (I expected Frank would say that.)

"No, where's he goin?" Joe asked.

"We know," Bob said. "Don't tell him, Frank."

"Aw, come on. You tell me, Chub. Where bouts you goin?"

"Tacoma," I answered.

"Tacoma! Who with?" Joe asked.

"Yeah, that's the joke of it. Who with?" Frank spoke in a way that made Bob laugh with him.

"Don't worry, Chub," Bob said soothingly. "She'll let you play with Elladine all you want to."

"You mean you're goin with Miss Love?" Joe exclaimed.

"Oh, no," Frank laughed. "She's goin with *him*. Isn't she, Chub?"

"She can if she wants to," I replied, affecting all the indifference I could muster.

"Yeah, but she can't go swimmin with you," Frank argued. "She'd sink like a rock, wearin a skirt like she does."

"Listen, Chub." Bob's voice was sympathetic now. "Frank's jealous cause *he* can't go to Tacoma. Me too! We have to stay here, same as always, in this hick town. There's never nothin to do around here. You think so, Joe?"

"Yeah, around here you always have to try to think of what to do. It's not that way in Tacoma. Say, I was just thinkin. . . . Why don't we climb up there on that ladder and take the rope off the school bell? Then Mr. Jones can't ring it, so they'll have to let school out a week sooner."

"Gee, that's a swell idea," Frank agreed. "It'll be celebratin for Chub leavin. We want him to think of all the fun he had with us when he's up there in Tacoma."

"Hear that, Chub? It's all account a your goin with Miss Love we're doin this. But we better wait till she goes home, before goin back in that schoolhouse," Bob advised.

"We have to wait till Mr. Jones goes, too," I insisted.

"Well then, we can have one more cigarette," Joe offered. "Look, there's only one left."

Each of us had a puff or two on Joe's cigarette. After that, we had a long time to watch and wait. So we moved over to where we could get a clear view of the road. Finally, we saw Miss Waite walk from the school's front door and come down the boardwalk. Some time after that, Miss Oaks and Miss Martin walked out and went up the road away from us. Then Mr. Hutchinson and Miss Love came walking together in our direction, as though they might be looking for us. When they were on the sidewalk nearest us, I was scared to death they would turn and come to find us. I wished we had stayed back at the pigpen where we could hide. Miss Love seemed so close I worried that she might even hear us breathing. The sun gleamed on her neatly rolled and knotted, very dark hair. She always had her arms folded. And her ground-length skirt swished as she walked. It then dawned on me, with a tinge of dismay, that I might soon be quite as near her as I was now near my friends crouched in the willows. It made me more eager to help silence the school bell before I had to go with her.

After we waited quite a while longer, I was relieved to hear Frank say, "There goes Mr. Jones across the road to where he lives. Now we can sneak up there."

To reach the school's side door, we had to ignore how noticeable we might be running across the yard — for it was broad daylight. The door was unlocked, so we were soon inside, confident our stealthiness had kept us from being seen by any adult. We quickly ran up the stairs to the second floor where high school and sixth, seventh and eighth grades were taught. There stood the tall ladder with its top end poking through a square hole in the ceiling. Seeing the darkness inside made me hesitate to get up into it. But Frank was already near the ladder's top and Bob, always wanting to help, was telling me:

"Go ahead, Chub, you're next! I'll be close behind so's to give you a boost."

I wasn't anxious for Bob's help, but I could never turn him down. I scrambled up the ladder and the four of us were soon standing on the rafters. Frank warned us not to step between them, or we would break through the plaster. That worried me. But I risked edging over close to the bell anyway. There it stood in its cupola, a lot bigger than I thought it was — and so silent. A knobbed tongue hung motionless inside it. Bob said it was what hit the bell to make it ring. There was the same rope that hung all the way downstairs for Mr. Jones to pull when it was time for us to line up. It was snugly wrapped around a big wheel, fastened to the side of the bell. Frank soon had it unwrapped.

"That will stop it from ringin," he laughed. "Now let's climb back down there and get out before Mr. Jones comes."

Getting down was a lot more scary than climbing up had been. I kept so close to Bob my feet grazed his hands all the way down. It felt good to get outside again. Mr. Nelson was going up the road on the way home from his day's work on the railroad. That meant I was already late for supper and would have some explaining to do when I got home. I went on the run, all the while trying to think of some permissible place I could have been spending time. Then it came to me. I'd say I walked up to the mill with Bob, and Mr. Fields asked us to come in and look around. It took longer than we expected. By the time they saw Mr. Fields to ask him, I'd be in Tacoma with Miss Love. At least that was one advantage in going with her. And with that consolation I went to bed with a conscience that let me sleep. The trouble came in my dream that found me up on the roof beside the bell, and when it began to move I began to fall.

Next morning after breakfast when Mama looked at the

clock, she wondered why the school bell wasn't ringing. We were ready to go, so she told us we had better get on to school anyway. I seemed to have an advantage in being the only one at home knowing why the bell kept silent, but I could see it was not going to keep school from opening.

Soon after we were in the schoolyard, Mr. Jones came to the front door with the iron triangle and beat it vigorously. It not only sounded worse than the bell, but earlier, too. In fact, it had a very impatient ring to it.

Whenever seated in our room, I imagined Miss Love was always looking straight at me. But at recess, Frank and Bob and Joe all said they thought she kept looking straight at them. Anyway the bell still kept silent, but the triangle called us back to our seats. Then suddenly there was a sound of violent splintering, followed by a jarring *thud* on the ceiling. Alarming as it sounded, I didn't dare to even move my head — much as I needed understanding looks from my partners in the last evening's venture upstairs. Miss Love hurried out of the room, but I still sat with my eyes straight ahead. Elladine sat beside me, and I knew she would detect and be eager to report any sign that my conscience was betraying me. Miss Love soon returned to the room, and things got back to normal. By noon, I was more than ready to hear the bell again and breathed with relief when it rang out as usual at half past twelve.

Near the end of the afternoon period we stood in line facing Miss Love seated behind her desk. I was always restless to get done with our reading lesson and especially this day to get out of the room and out of sight of the school. When back in our seats Miss Love at last stood up to dismiss us, but as usual she first had a special instruction to give.

"Frank, Robert, Joseph and Gordon will all remain in their seats. Except for them, the room is dismissed."

After all but we four had marched out, the stillness in the

room got so painful to stay in that Miss Love's voice seemed almost soothing.

"Frank, Robert and Joseph, your fathers are coming to Mr. Hutchinson's office. You may go up there now and wait for them."

When they left the room I was more scared than ever. And I about sank through the floor when I saw Miss Love go and open the lower drawer of her desk. I knew only too well what she kept in it! She sat in her chair and ordered me to come to her. I stood up and then took the shortest and slowest steps I could take, but it seemed there was hardly any distance to go. She had her arms folded and the ever impressive strap laid across her lap. I clasped my hands and stood as straight as I could.

"Gordon, both Mr. Jones and Mrs. Jones said they saw you boys running down the upper stairs after everyone else had gone home yesterday evening. Now if you tell me a story, you shall be punished more severely than if you tell me the truth. I want you to tell me whether with Frank, Robert and Joseph you climbed that ladder up to where the bell is. And I want the *truth*," Miss Love commanded, taking the strap in her hand.

I could see I had better own up, so I said, "Yes, we was up there, I guess."

"Oh, so you were! Well, I am sure they will get the truth out of the others, too. You shall not be punished now, but we are going to see your mother and, I trust, your father immediately. I have in mind what is best to do with you."

As we started for home, Miss Love said, "You are to walk as fast as your legs can carry you," and in no time at all, I was beside her doing just that.

My mother was sitting in the parlor with Mrs. Hahn who, at that moment, I fervently wished could be my schoolteacher. Looking surprised, my mother asked, "What is the trouble now? . . . There is the chair you always like, Myra."

Miss Love had my hand in hers as she stepped over to sit facing my mother.

"Well, Mary, either I must first tell you what Gordon and three other of my boys did, or someone else will. They climbed up a tall ladder to the school bell and got the rope off of it. That is why the bell kept silent this morning."

"Oh, goodness, what shall we do!" my mother exclaimed. "I hope this does not make him too much for you to take care of this summer."

"Never doubt that," Miss Love emphasized with a shake of her head. "But the worst of this was that Mr. Hutchinson had to climb up into the bell attic, where he accidentally stepped onto the plaster ceiling. There was a desk for his feet to land on and shorten his fall — without injury, thank goodness."

"Well!" My mother assured Miss Love. "We'll have to help pay for that. I feel very fortunate no one was injured."

"Yes," Miss Love consoled, "I know you would want to do that. Gordon has not been punished yet. I had a notion to spank him, but that ought to be done for his own mischief than for following those older boys into theirs. I think, though, it would be well for him to come and stay with me during the next three days. As you know, we expect to leave early Saturday morning for Tacoma, so you should not have to worry about him, all summer long at least. Mr. Smith will take us in his hack directly to the Milwaukee depot."

"Oh, I see what you mean," my mother said. "You would not wait until you leave to have him in your care. Well, it's up to you. . . . I don't like having him away but Mrs. Hahn who has to keep track of him won't mind."

"It seems that is the only way I know to keep Gordon out

of more trouble this last week, Mary. I would not want to lose him before we are started!"

"Oh, Myra, you are like one of our family! Of course, Gordon loves you, too. But you know how boys are at his age. They never let on."

"Yes, I know," Miss Love said with a smile, as she guided me to sit on her lap. "And I am sorry Gordon shall have to realize he too must be punished. *That* shall begin on the way to my house now. So kiss your mother good night, Gordon, and come along."

Out on the sidewalk Miss Love said sharply, "Now you march straight ahead of me, Gordon. You know where my house is."

Yes, I knew where it was, and I knew it was the last place I wanted to go, but I could not go any other place with Miss Love right behind me. Ahead of us I could see Arlie with belly down on the ditch bank and one arm in the water. If only I had been with him instead of with Frank, I thought. Without taking his arm from the water, Arlie turned his face my way. He was dredging for pennywinkles. A few of them were in a can beside him. I reached down to get one for company, but the tone of Miss Love's voice changed my mind.

"Gordon! You march! I am going to ask Mr. Ruth for a switch off his peach tree."

He was one we boys like to tease, so I knew he would be glad to oblige Miss Love this time. As soon as we got to his gate, Miss Love told me to stay in place. Then she un-latched and opened the gate and walked up to Mr. Ruth who was seated on his front step. He quickly rose, and it seemed only a word was needed from her for him to soon be at a tree with his jackknife in hand, cutting off a switch she pointed to. After cleanly trimming it, he handed it to her. When on our way again, I imagined that she carried it under her folded arms, and I knew the only way to keep it there was for me not to dally on the way again.

When we finally got to Miss Love's gate, I saw Elladine sitting in a swing. Miss Love opened the gate and guided me inside.

Elladine came over to us. "Hello, Auntie," she said. "Hello, Gordon. Did Auntie bring you to play with me?"

"Yes, Elladine, Gordon may sometimes play here with you this week. He was a very bad boy yesterday, so Auntie wants to keep him with her where he shall have to be good. He may play with you in the yard while I get his bath ready. Only in *this* yard now, Elladine," Miss Love called from the door of the house.

"Yes, Auntie, I know. . . . Remember, Gordon, what Auntie said. We can't go out on the road, or back there to the millpond either! But we can go over to the swing and you can push me."

The way she was always saying "Auntie" made me desperate to get out of hearing distance, but it seemed more prudent to go with her to the swing. She sat in it and I pushed so lazily that she swung within easy talking distance.

"Gordon, what did you do bad again yesterday that Auntie said you did?"

"Be quiet. I can't stand how you say that. I hate that name for her."

"Well, then, what did you do bad?"

"What d'you think?"

"Oh, probably you were chewing tobacco." (She knew it made me sick.) "Or maybe you put a frog down Wanda's neck again."

"Naw!"

"Did she give you a lickin?"

"Not this time."

"It mustn't have been very bad then."

"Oh? You think so? How come the bell didn't ring this morning?"

"Chub! Did you do that?"

"Sure! Me'n some other kids."

"How could you climb all the way up where the bell is?"

"Aw, it's not —"

"Gorduuunn! Come innn!"

"There!" Elladine exclaimed. "Auntie called. You better run."

Elladine always had to know what was good for me, so I ran with all speed to Miss Love who was standing in the front door. Elladine's mother, who also stood there, greeted me:

"How do you do, Gordon? It is nice to see you playing in our yard with Elladine."

"Yes, it is," Miss Love added. "But now, Gordon, I want you to come with me. I have ready for you just the kind of bath you need, after climbing up into that dusty, sooty attic to untie the bell."

Miss Love now wore an apron of gray calico with a ruffle that drooped below her knees. She directed me through the parlor and dining room into the kitchen, then into a smaller room where a steaming tub was sitting on a bench. A footstool was near it.

"Get your shoes and stockings off, Gordon. And your pants and shirt, too. You surely do need a good bath. I found out you were even in that pen with a lot of pigs yesterday. I know your mother did not know about that. Hurry up now. Here, I will unbutton your shirt. Now your union suit. This is a good time for you to learn what bath time will be like this summer."

The kind of bath Miss Love then gave me I thought she must have invented to make me wish I had stayed out of any pigpen or attic. By the time she was through, I smarted as though she had left no skin on me. I was in no frame of mind to hear her say:

"Gordon, we did not bring your nightgown, or whatever you wear in bed. But I have a nightgown for you to wear. Dressed in it, you will not want to run off with anyone like Frank, I am quite sure. I want you to wear these underpants with it. There . . . now this goes over your head like that. . . . It buttons here in back. . . . Get this calico apron on next . . . to protect your nightgown until bedtime, and that will be sooner than you expect. Your hair is badly in need of combing, so come into the bedroom with Auntie. Would you like to call me 'Auntie' — the way Elladine does?"

I shook my head *no* as hard as I could.

"Well . . . we shall see about that a little later. . . . Here we are in our bedroom. That little bed in the corner is yours. A curtain goes around it. Sit in that chair please, while I brush and comb your hair. . . . It surely needs some attention. . . . Now hold perfectly still. . . . You will find that Auntie wants a boy's hair kept in good order."

I thought she would never get through fussing with my hair. Then at last she let up on it and said:

"There, Gordon, I want you to try to keep your hair just as neat as it is now. You may sit in that chair by the window and read from this book of Bible stories. You can never know them well enough. But this summer we shall try to. In the next half hour I want to visit with Elladine and her mother. I may be back in here anytime, so remember what I have told you."

After a few minutes, I was looking out on the road or at the cows in the pasture beyond it. Mr. Wallace drove by standing on an empty hayrack. Suddenly I had to blink my eyes on seeing Frank and Bob strolling along the road. They did not turn their heads to look my way until they were past the house. They gave me a quick look and then were soon up the road behind the trees. I thought of sneaking out the window after them, but the familiar tone of a voice I could very clearly hear from the other room kept me prudently in my seat. And it prompted me to go on looking at the pictures in the book until, in a while, I could hardly keep my eyes open. They opened up, though, when I heard Miss Love at the door, saying:

"You may put your book on that table and come out here, Gordon. It is time for supper."

An aroma of food cooking that I could not resist had come into the room, in spite of my dislike to be seen wearing a nightgown. Harold and Douglas, to my joy, were not at the table. Elladine, her mother and Miss Love were.

Elladine's mother announced that Harold and Douglas had eaten early and gone fishing in the millpond.

"I hope they catch something good to eat, but I miss having supper with them, and I wanted Gordon to see them," Miss Love said.

I only wished I could kick her shin for wanting them to see me just then. She and Elladine's mother continued talking about the bell, and then Miss Love added:

"Mr. Hutchinson wanted me to punish Gordon at school, but when I told him Gordon would feel it was punishment to be under my thumb the next few days, he was thoroughly satisfied."

"Myra, will Gordon be going to bed early?"

"Yes, indeed! He shall be in bed in a very short time. Why?"

"Oh, I wondered whether he would be up to play with Elladine. I am going to see Mrs. Roan for a few minutes, so now I shall take her with me. You believe in having children in bed early, don't you, Myra?"

"I most certainly do. When Elladine stays with me she is

in bed early, too. But you have never heard her complain of that."

"No, I must say I haven't."

"Elladine and Gordon can be together all day long. That is time enough without them staying up at night to play. Well, if you will excuse us, I want Gordon to learn a short verse from the Bible and, after saying his prayers, go to bed."

Long after I was in bed, I heard laughter in the yard that I could tell came from Elladine, for one. I itched to get up and see what there was to laugh at, but Miss Love was liable to look in on me, as she had been doing almost every minute, it seemed. In time, it quieted down out in the yard, and pretty soon I heard what sounded like Elladine running upstairs. When at last I thought she was in bed, I settled down and went to sleep.

Miss Love roused me from sleep and said, "Time to get up, Gordon." I could not wait to get out of the nightgown and into my school clothes, which happily had not been replaced in the night. Breakfast hit the spot. Once it was over, Miss Love was soon out the front door with Elladine and me hurrying to keep up with her. At the gate she waited, then motioned for us to step in front of her.

"Take each other's hand, children. I want you to go before me. March just as you do in school. That is the way. Gordon, watch your step. There is to be no getting out of line for you."

Walking hand in hand with Elladine to school, with Miss Love behind to watch our every step, made me think the devil was grinning with glee from the cupola he had gotten me up to on Monday. Anyway, I kept looking up at it, wondering. I was still wondering when we met Mr. Hutchinson in front of the schoolhouse.

"Good morning, Miss Love and Elladine. And who is this?"

"It is Gordon, Mr. Hutchinson." (That seemed to startle him.)

"Gordon! Well, this must be the first time I have seen him not a bit concealed by so much hair. You did a good job on it, Miss Love."

"Yes, it took a little work," Miss Love replied as Mr. Hutchinson stepped beside her, and we marched up the walk into the schoolhouse as the bell began to ring. And this morning, I was glad it could ring again. There was still half an hour, Miss Love said, for Elladine and me to play. That, of course, was "together" and within a certain area where Miss Love could keep her eyes on us.

The two other days in Miss Love's care at Thorp were no more fun than the first one. Nothing, though, seemed to spoil my dream of spending a summer in Tacoma.

Chapter 17

OVER THE FALLS

On the evening before Miss Love and I were going on the train, I was in bed gazing through the open window. The sun, magnified in burnished gold, was nearly touching the horizon. The dashing, frothing waterfall at the mills sang to me. But soon Nelson Mills opened the gate that let water rush down to power the wheel. Then the *grumble-gramble* rhythm of the gear, whirling the dynamo, mingled with the sound of the water. No. 42 came whooshing and bounding down the rails and whistled to signal it would stop at Thorp. It brought things to see: people getting off and on; cans of cream and sacks of mail being loaded; steam bursting out of the piston cylinder; flashes from the firebox; and the engineer reaching to his throttle. I closed my eyes and listened to 42 *puff-puff, puff-puff-puff* as it raced off to Ellensburg.

Still half awake, I dreamed of the times we trudged on the dirt path or road half a mile to the millpond. We could go in swimming there, or maybe skip over the floating logs, unless we got on a three-plank raft and poled to the other end of the pond. Or we might listen to the millrace below the falls as we fished for rainbow trout. We heard the waterwheel labor and the sawmill hum. We saw Mr. Mills (that was his true name) standing by a wooden lever that he rocked back and forth to move the carriage carrying a log its full length into the screaming teeth of the tall spinning saw. When the board fell free, Nelson rolled it away.

Across the waterfall stood the three-story flour mill. It

had mystery and an inviting smell inside, where everything was white with flour, including Mr. Kendall and his helper, Henry. We would get inside, even though Mr. Kendall never seemed glad to see us. He never had any kids of his own. One day, soon after there had been a flood, he was hauling his Tip Top flour to load in a boxcar when his bay team mired up to their bellies across from our store.

I dreamed of going skating on the millpond. Sometimes we waded through a foot of snow to get there. It was more fun to hook our sleds onto a bobsled. One snowy day my brother Charles made a sled out of boards. It was big enough for several of us to sit in and be pulled by Happy, our bay white-faced horse. When hitched she sniffed the air and frisked off as though she liked it as much as we did. Other times, one or two of us rode her bareback. Happy would not carry us willingly more than a few blocks from her barn. When it seemed to her the road was leaving Thorp, she turned first one way and then the other and tended to rear up until she got her course reversed, and then wasted no time on the return home. For though plump and lazy, there was no horse around who could pass Happy on her way to the barn where she always remembered the chopped wheat was kept. Before Happy, we had another gentle horse named Sam. One day, when I was up barely clinging to his back, Ethel Harper — much older than me — jumped out and made him sidestep. I fell off.

A voice roused me from my dream. It was Elladine's mother saying, "Myra, you'll have your hands full this summer."

"Yes, but not more full than I like to have them."

"Well, Myra, I'd hate to be responsible for the antics of that boy in the city all summer long. He won't know where to stop."

"Yes, Eleanor, but that is what he has to be taught: *where to stop!*"

"And I don't know anyone who knows as well as you how to teach him, Myra. Tell me about those two boys you had one summer. What were their names?"

"John and Paul. And if you ever saw two little rascals, it was them. Lloyd came to join them before the summer was too far gone. None of them had ever had proper training. But that made it all the more worthwhile for me to give them the attention they surely needed. I would love having several children who needed care this summer."

"I know you would, Myra, and you will have two who do, after Elladine comes over there next week with me. You may find they are enough. Oh, I just know you will all have a wonderful summer in Tacoma, while I am in Alaska. What do you think Gordon will do when he sees all those nice clothes you have made for him?"

"What will he do? Why . . . he will wear them of course. I did not do all that work for nothing. I cannot wait to see Elladine and him side-by-side in their middy blouses."

"That will tickle Elladine, too, and I expect Gordon will soon get used to wearing his."

"Yes, Eleanor, he most certainly shall get used to it and to many other improvements while he is in my care."

"When did you decide to take Gordon with you to Tacoma, Myra?"

"It was that day he and Frank led Elladine up into Wyatt's barn loft. I told you before how it was. Remember? After the boys persuaded her to climb a ladder up to a high ledge with them, they slipped down quickly and pulled the ladder away. I shall never forget how worried I was before we found her. She was frightened out of her wits. I determined right then and there what it was Gordon needed and I would see to it that he got just that. I felt he had long been asking, unintentionally, for me to give him more care than I could give him in school."

"How did you know his father and mother would agree with you?"

"They knew of my concern for Gordon and that I would give him the attention they could not give him until his mother was in better health. It will be good for Elladine as well as for me to have him. But most of all, it will be good for Gordon. You shall see how quickly he will learn how to play with Elladine. There will be no Frank or Robert there for him to get in mischief with. You may rest assured of that."

"Uncle and Aunt won't be there, will they?"

"No, they were leaving this week to spend the summer in Michigan."

"You will still have the company of Luella and Mr. Jim, won't you? Don't you love to hear Mr. Jim spin a yarn in that backwoods style of his? I hope you let Gordon get to know him. Is Luella glad you are bringing the children?"

"Yes, she has urged me to bring them."

"Does she help you with their care?"

"Yes, in that she does most of the cooking and I can leave the children with her, whenever necessary. Luella asked for a leave of absence from the library in order to spend this summer at home with us. She thinks children in her house are fine — when *I* am responsible for them," Miss Love said with a laugh.

"Well, she is some years younger and has had none of the experience with children that we have had. Myra, it is warm enough, so why don't we sit out in the front yard awhile?"

"That suits me, but first I want to look at Gordon. I hope he is asleep."

As Miss Love tiptoed near my bed, I tried to lie and breathe as though asleep. She carefully tucked in the sheet around me. Soon I heard her leaving the room and then the sound of her voice through the open front window. I jumped out of bed with a good idea of what I wanted to do. I thought:

Where'd she put my clothes? . . . Oh, here they are. . . . I have to get out of this nightgown. . . . There, I'm dressed. . . . I wonder where's my shoes. . . . I don't see them. . . . Guess I'll go barefooted, then they won't hear me walking. . . . Here's the kitchen and the door is even open. . . . From here it's easy getting to the bank of the millpond. . . . I wish I'd run into Frank and Bob. . . . The water isn't so wide here. . . . It goes into the mill, so's to turn the dynamo I hear now. . . . How can I get across and get down there on the road that bends around the mills? . . . The water's so deep and dark, I'm scared to get in it. But, if I took the road out in front of the mills, she'd see me. I got to get across this water someway. Then I can get on the road behind the mill out of sight. If only Frank and Bob were here, they'd know how to.

If I walk on this bank clear to the mill, maybe something'll show up. It's hard walking barefoot when it's kind a dark, but lucky the moon is shining big. . . . Oh, here's where the pond goes in under the mill, and there's the waterfall rushing down over the chutes. . . . This is the last place to cross, so they don't see me. . . . It's worse than ever here. . . . I was even scared being here in the daytime with Frank and Bob. . . . But I got to get across there, or I'll never find them till they've gone to bed. . . . I've got an idea. That board stretches clear across the top of the falls to the other side. It's big as a railroad tie and a lot longer. I won't get so scared with my eyes shut and feeling with my bare feet. . . . Well, here goes. . . . This ain't so bad. It's a good thing I never found my shoes. With them on I couldn't a done this.

Barefooted, there's no chance a slipping by just keeping one foot in ahead a the other. . . . I must be halfway already —

"Gorduuunn! How dare you! For mercy's sake!"

Oh, oh, she sees me. . . . Now I'm in it. . . . What'll I do? . . . Guess I'll jump in and see if I can float to the mill. . . . Gee, this water's cold. . . . I must be in the falls . . . and it's taking me down! . . . That hurt, hitting these hard boards. Now I'm sliding. . . . Down again. . . . Ouch! . . . These boards are sure slippery. Here's another drop. . . . I can't hardly breathe in this foaming water. . . . At last I'm out of it and there's the bank I can get on. Anything is better than up on the bank where she is. I'll never do this again.

"Gordon, I see you down there! I want you to walk along near the water until you can step up here where I am. Do you hear me!"

"Yes, ma'am, I hear." My teeth chattered.

"Can you get up this bank?"

"Yes, ma'am. I think so."

"Well, if I have to come down there, you *will* move faster."

I climbed up in a hurry to where Miss Love stood with a switch in her hand. But I couldn't imagine anything she could do being worse than going down that waterfall.

"Gordon, what am I going to do with you! You are soaking wet! It is a miracle you were not drowned tumbling down that waterfall. Now you march back to the house and into that room where I left you in your bed. I ought to blister you, and I still may do just that. I never was so frightened in all my life! And to think that you would be so daring in Aunt Eleanor's house. You had better march quickly!"

So I got back into the bedroom in a lot less time than it had taken me in getting to the waterfall. Only Miss Love was there with me, so I couldn't hope anyone would in-

fluence her to change what I feared she had in mind. I
sighed with relief when she laid her switch on the table and
began to take my wet clothes off. Soon I was dry and even
glad to be in another nightgown. But I took alarm all over
again when she, after taking up her hairbrush, got into
position on the chair. Never before had I stood facing her
feeling so defenseless, nor had she ever seemed more determined. How I wished then that I'd stayed in bed. But I
hadn't.

"Gordon, if you ever needed to be punished, you surely
need to be now. Do you know that?"

"Yes, ma'am . . . I think so . . . maybe."

"You *knew* it was wrong to get out of bed?"

"Yes, ma'am . . . you said not to. . . ."

"But you stole out and ran away — nearly losing your
life. Since I shall be responsible for you all of this summer,
it is plain that I shall have to teach you how to mind me —
much better than I have done."

With the hairbrush, Miss Love kept tapping the palm of
her hand. I could not avoid gazing into her harrowing dark
eyes. I put my hands behind me, useless as I knew that was,
to prepare for what was coming. I could only hope that her
seeing me so scared would make her go easy. Then, to my
unspeakable relief, she laid the hairbrush on her lap and
reached back of her head with both hands, as though to
make sure her hair was still neatly done up in a knot. Then
she said:

"Gordon, if I were to give you the spanking you well
deserve, you would not want to sit down for a week. But to
save spoiling our trip, I am going to let you go without it for
now, and I pray you will not soon again give me any reason
to punish you. You will still have to tell Aunt Eleanor you
are sorry for being so naughty and say the prayer I have

taught you for her to hear. And you will have to repeat the same apology and prayer for me to hear."

Miss Love then had me practice my apology and instructed me how to say my prayer for Elladine's mother. That seemed worse to me than maybe getting a spanking, but then I was sure I didn't want anything like that with her hairbrush.

"Eleanor, Gordon has something to tell you."

"Oh? That's nice. Come over here and tell me, Gordon. . . . That's a good boy. What have you to say?"

"I'm sorry I got out of bed and I will not ever be so naughty again." *I never thought anyone could make me go through this stuff.*

"Dear Jesus, bless Mama, Papa, Aunt Eleanor, Auntie and everyone. I will do Your holy will, so I may see You in heaven someday. Thank You for all the love and care I get. Please help other boys and girls the way You help me. With Your help it is easy for me to always be good. Amen."

After I repeated my apology and prayer in a similar manner for Miss Love, she directed me to bed and tucked me in again. It was good to be in bed after such a close call going over the falls. But getting out of a lickin from Miss Love was even better. I'd never try her out anymore, I decided, and went to sleep.

Chapter 18

THE DAY COMES

Early the next morning I sat beside Miss Love on the back seat of a topless buggy going to catch the train for Tacoma. It was not a situation that made me feel at home, but I was confident that once we were on the train going like the wind, it would be easy to keep out of her sight. I was glad the day had come for us to leave, even though she appeared more forbidding than ever, her erect figure close beside me. I knew there were lots of kids in Tacoma for me to join in play and mischief more enticing than in Thorp. I wondered what the swimming hole would be like. Cities had lots of swimming holes. If only Frank and Bob were going with me. But they never had the chance, even if they wanted to.

We were going on the Milwaukee Railroad and the depot was over a mile away. As we rode past the Snyder place I saw George driving the cows out of the meadow to the barn where he would have to feed the calves and turn the cream separator. He waved at me, and I waved back. I thought he must be wishing that he was going away on the train instead of having to tramp with his bare feet in a lot of manure. I'd hate to have to stay out on a farm the way he had to, without any kids like there were in Thorp to go swimming with.

"Well, Gordon, this is the morning we have looked forward to, isn't it?"

"Yes, ma'am. . . . I think so."

"Are you glad vacation is here?"

"Uh, huh. Are there any kids around there to have fun with?"

"Ho, ho, ho! Don't you think that you have had enough of that to last you for a while?"

I shook my head.

"Oh, yes! But of course you will have enough company. The *nicest* kind of company, too. I expect you are going to have the best summer ever, and your mama will have plenty of time to get back to feeling well again, without having to worry about you."

"Where can I go swimming then?"

"Oh, Gordon, in the city there will be so many things for you to do, I don't think you will have time for swimming. . . . Here we are already at the depot. . . . The train is nearly due."

When we stopped, I leaped out and ran toward the platform. I saw Mr. Apgard, with his heavy eyebrows and dark gray mustache, wearing the little stiff-billed cap with AGENT on it. He was peering down the railroad track, as if trying to be the first to spy the approaching train.

"Oh, hello there, Chub," he said, hardly turning his head. "Where you going? What is it? . . . You going along with Miss Love?"

"Uh huh . . . sorta," I answered.

"Well, good morning, ma'am."

"Yes, it is a beautiful morning, Mr. Apgard. Will you have our things put on the train?"

"Yes, ma'am . . . sure, ma'am . . . sure will. . . . Do it myself. . . . I see Chub here is going with you. That's something I never thought of. . . . Bet you and him get along good. . . . Of course boys his size get a bit frisky now and then, you know." Mr. Apgard was looking sideways at me, as he reminded Miss Love of what she might be in for.

"Yes, Mr. Apgard, I have heard that." Miss Love beamed down at me.

Soon the rails began to waken and hum with vibrant new life. The train was not far away. I could see it bending on the curve, then coming straight and black as an iron rod, wearing its smokestack like a tall hat atop its single eye, pushing the cowcatcher ahead to shoo off anything on the rails. It kept coming on, bearing down the straight track, getting bigger, bigger, bigger and then the engine *whooshed* by with a thundering noise and a burst of wind, its bell *ding-ding-danging* and its wheels clanking on the rails as fire flashed beneath the cab. I shivered with excitement to see the goggled engineer, in blue and red, bob by with his hand reached to the throttle. When the train stopped I could hear the locomotive breathing. Then a cloud of steam bloomed out from it.

The sounds and odors carried me away. I forgot I was with someone — until I came to at the familiar snap of a finger in a faintly perfumed presence, as a lacy white handkerchief fluttered near me.

Miss Love snapped, "Gordon, give me your hand!"

Not waiting, she reached down and grasped my hand, firmly drawing me next to her as she hurried onto the train. She kept me thus secured until we reached the section reserved for us. Looks of amusement from passengers along the aisle added to my abashment. At first I meant to rebel, but the train was underway and Miss Love's determined looks and actions quickly dispelled my rash impulse.

She guided me into a compartment and then drew the curtains, leaving only the window side open. She pointed to the seat, where I then sat and looked out as the train began moving.

It all looks familiar to me. There is Newman's red livery barn way over there. . . . Two horses are in the corral. . . .

*Hidden in that brush near the barn is the swimming hole.
. . . Nobody's there and it's lonely this time of the morning.
Probably Frank and Bob, besides Joe and Arlie, will be
coming there later on today. Maybe they'll wonder where I
am. I suppose they'll be there every day from now on. Oh
well, maybe they wish they were on this train too. I wish
they were.*

*I can see the depot across from our store. Bill must be
there sweeping out now. He said it looked to him like it
would be pretty quiet around there with me gone this summer. . . . There's the school. . . . At least I'd rather be on this
train than in school. . . . I think. . . . The church is next. . . .
No one is near it this morning. . . . This train is going pretty
fast it looks like. . . . We're passing the mills already and I
can see that board I fell off last night. . . . A lot farther from
here, I see the bridge Frank and Bob and me got stuck on
one time riding on a freight train. We walked all the way
back and around to Thorp on that hill. . . . We're sure going
fast now. . . . I guess the train's in a hurry to get to Tacoma.
. . . I wonder who lives in that house. . . . Things along here
don't look like anything I ever saw before. But I can see
Miss Love in this window looking the same as she did back
there in school. . . . There's her hand on my shoulder. . . .
Now what's she doing? . . . Imagine! That's her patting my
cheek, and she's breathing close to the back of my neck!*

"Gordon, this summer you will see and learn many
things. Elladine will come next week with her mother to be
the very nicest playmate you ever had. Then, in no time at
all, our summer will be over and you will be watching out
the window — hardly able to wait as our train coming back
to Thorp whistles to stop there and let us off. Turn around
here now, your hair needs to be combed."

She tore into my hair with brush and comb, as though it
had offended her and as if to show how differently it would

be kept in Tacoma. Even that could not dispel my dream of adventures and mysteries in places far away, for once, from the bawling calves and cackling chickens that often had wakened me back there in Thorp.

Chapter 19

IN THIS ROOM

Time has sped by since that trip to Tacoma on the Milwaukee when I was eight. Now we have children and grandchildren living near us in Seattle. Back here in Thorp I slept last night in that next room where my parents slept from the time I was two. It's where Ma died in 1954 at age eighty-two and Pa in 1960 at one hundred and one. They moved from the Pacific coast to this dry climate hoping it would improve Ma's health. My older brother was six and the younger was three months old then. Ma stayed the previous winter with two of us in Cle Elum, eighteen miles west of here and higher in the mountains. The doctor afterward recommended Thorp's altitude of 1,640 feet for her.

Pa came out to Montesano, Washington from Pepin, Wisconsin in 1889, and Ma from Osceola, Iowa in 1892. Pa was seven, the oldest of five children, when his father died leaving them penniless. One time he told me, "Mind you, when I got a nickel, I took it home and gave it to my mother." He attended about three years of school, he said, but two of his sisters became public school teachers. In Wisconsin he worked in summer as a carpenter and in winter as a blacksmith at two and a half dollars a day, when common labor was paid one dollar. He served on the Thorp school board as long as he had a child in the school. In 1880 he voted for Garfield and the Republican party but after that joined the Democratic party as though it were a lodge, believing it would do most for the common man. In early days around here he said many thought a Democrat and a horse thief were about alike. Many times he would be one of only two or three at a county caucus. When flat on that bed in there, only days before death came, he said to me, "Yes, I remember like it was yesterday hearing them talk about Lincoln being shot." That had been ninety-five years before when Pa was six years old. He always considered himself a Christian but never got around to being baptized in a church. He had only a few days to live when a friend who worked at the depot across the street came to baptize him in her faith. As though to tell her he had had baptism enough for his need, he was overheard saying to the lady whom he had long valued as a friend, "I'm not afraid to die." He had lived then nearly sixty years in this room.

In this room is where Ma spent much of her life and where we delighted in her baked beans, apple pie and in all those other good things she enjoyed making for us. She was always faithful to her church and read more than one Bible until its cover was frayed. All the time I was away from home, after I was eighteen, she sat there and typed a letter to me every week she was able. She never let me know of the times she could hardly get up from bed to do it. Those hundreds of letters have been saved. Ma also had much good health and then made friends for our whole family. I think no one could love children more than she did and she and Pa for many years had the love of four grandchildren.

My brother has lived here since he was six. That must be a record for continuous tenancy in this county. He seems to remember everything he ever learned in school. Today he's out to catch a swarm of bees seceded from one of his hives and looking for a new home. He will give them one and in the fall rob them of all the honey they can bring in above their need for winter. He has been keeping bees since 1912. Now he only keeps 75 hives instead of the 250 he once had.

One day's work in an apiary gave me enough experience with bees. My brother is also a retired railway mail clerk. Any of them still living are retired, I think.

This morning I walked up the road to the old flour mill. There isn't so much water coming over the falls as there was the evening I tried to walk across it and fell in on seeing Miss Love motioning to me from below. I tried to swim away from her but the pull of the falls was too much. Wanting to reflect on that adventure and on others, I went this morning and sat on the bank of the millpond. I never knew when in school of Miss Myra Love's first love affair or of what it had done to her. But my Aunt Lib, who was Myra's close friend at normal school, knew about it and long afterward told me the story of "The Minister's Daughter."

Chapter 20

THE MINISTER'S DAUGHTER

No medicine or prayer, or loved one's dearest need for her could save Bernice Love from the pitiless ravages of typhoid fever in 1880. It left Myra, a smiling affectionate little girl, age five, without a mother. But fortunately her father's sister, Auntie, who cared for Myra's mother in her illness, stayed to raise Myra with her six-year-old adopted son. Always puritanical as she could be, Auntie had an exceptional love for children that would have a profound influence on Myra.

Myra had two brothers and one sister some ten years older than she was. All lived in or near Richdale which was situated in a rich, beautiful valley of irrigated hay and grain farms. A few years before Myra was born, her father had been a part-time circuit rider. Then for many years he had charge of a church at Richdale. When Myra was twelve, her father was called to the pastorship of a prosperous church at Ellensburg, a hundred miles from Richdale.

Myra always attended Sunday school and the preaching service on Sunday morning. She sang in the choir and learned to play the church organ. On Sunday evenings there was a young people's conference and then another preaching service for her to enjoy. Myra never wanted to miss the prayer meeting held in the church on Thursday evening. Her father would often repeat a prayer, reading in part: "Oh merciful God, grant that all carnal affections may die in us, and that all things belonging to the Spirit may live

and grow in us. Grant that we may have power and strength
to have victory, and triumph against the devil, the world,
and the flesh." Myra loved to hear that.

The social functions Myra attended in church were always restrained and orderly. When the elders at last voted
to allow a basket auction in the church hall, there were
many members who insisted *the devil himself* had been invited to come in.

After Myra completed two years of high school, she entered the State Normal School to become a teacher. The
normal school, offering study courses equivalent to two years
of college, was even closer to the parsonage where she lived
than was the high school. At the age of eighteen, Myra
graduated from normal school. The school recommended
highly that she be hired to teach public school. Myra, however, chose to assist in the operation of a small Christian
boarding school for children up to the fifth grade. After two
terms in that work she decided to teach public school.

On a Sunday morning in late June, after playing the
organ for the singing of "What a Friend We Have in Jesus,"
Myra sat with her arms folded and glanced around, as though
in search of someone. Her brilliant dark eyes came to rest
on the handsome face of a young man with wavy reddish
hair sitting on the end of the fifth row of the aisle nearest
the organ. His eyes had been fixed on Myra almost without
a waver, ever since he'd walked down the aisle to his seat.
Now, as her brown eyes met his blue eyes, it gave each a
start. Myra averted her eyes with a long, steady glance to the
door at the rear of the church. She remembered having seen
the young man working in Young's Drug Store and knew his
name was Bruce Calkins, a newcomer in Ellensburg.

After the benediction, Bruce moved back up the aisle to

the vestibule, in no hurry to leave. His thoughts were on Myra and how he could contrive to ask her to go for a Sunday afternoon walk. He met Mr. and Mrs. Shoebridge, for whom he had filled prescriptions at the drugstore. Mr. Shoebridge, an elder of the church, said, "Oh, it's Bruce. Very glad you could hear our service this morning, Bruce. Hope you will join us next Sunday — the Lord willing."

"I would like to," Bruce replied. "It was a good sermon this morning and the kind of music I like to hear."

But Bruce could *really* only hear the sounds of summer and smell its perfume floating in from the surrounding meadows and gardens through the opened windows of the church; just as he could see only Myra's flashing dark eyes behind the organ in the vision still before him.

Myra had watched Bruce go into the vestibule out of sight, as wonderingly she sat on the organ bench. When the church was nearly emptied, she took her purse and handkerchief and hurried up the aisle, hoping to get another glimpse of him. In the vestibule she was first glad, then embarrassed, as she encountered Bruce talking to Mr. and Mrs. Shoebridge.

"Oh, here is our Myra," Mrs. Shoebridge exclaimed happily. "She plays the organ so beautifully for us. Myra, have you met Mr. Bruce Calkins?"

Myra looked at Bruce with a smile and shook her head.

"Bruce, I would like to have you meet Miss Love, Miss Myra Love. . . . Miss Love, please meet Mr. Bruce Calkins, our friend at the drugstore."

After a few more friendly words, Mr. and Mrs. Shoebridge, with commendable discernment and consideration, remembered it was time for them to get on home for dinner. That put Myra and Bruce a little more at ease as they smiled at each other.

"I wonder where you . . . that is — learned how to play

the organ so — good as I ever heard anyway?" Bruce stammered, then smiled again.

"Thank you for saying that. Auntie taught me first of all, and then I took lessons at the Normal. But I'm just the substitute. Mrs. Ames will be back next month. She is an organ teacher," Myra explained.

As though by prearrangement, Myra and Bruce walked slowly out of the church together. When they reached the sidewalk, Myra turned to go to the parsonage next to the church. Bruce lingered at her side.

"It's been so long since I ate breakfast, I guess I'll go and get some dinner to take its place," Bruce said casually.

"Where do you eat?" Myra asked.

"Oh, generally at the City Cafe."

"Well, we can't serve you like the City Cafe does, but today we are having a pot roast. Would you like to share it with us?"

"Gee, that's the best thing I've heard since you played the organ!" Bruce exclaimed.

The Reverend Love and Auntie welcomed Bruce most cordially, but all during dinner Bruce hardly saw them. He saw only Myra's brown eyes and her wealth of dark hair with its sheeny softness, and hoped they could be alone on the riverbank some evening very soon. It would be a dream there with her, when the smell of mowed-that-day alfalfa hay curing in the nearby fields sweetened the warm evening air, and the full moon was in the eastern sky.

On Wednesday, Bruce got off work early. He hurried to the livery stable a few blocks away. When he got there, Burt was hitching Dick, a white-faced chestnut, to a topless buggy. Bruce jumped up into the seat and picked up the reins. Myra had promised she would go with him to the river for a picnic, two miles away. Bruce could hardly wait. It was a perfect June day with not a fleck in the blue sky.

Bruce drove up in front of the parsonage and Myra soon appeared carrying a basket. He jumped down, took the basket and put it on top of the lap robe behind the seat. He hurried to help Myra up into the seat, but she had climbed up before he could reach her. This was almost the first time Myra had gone out with a man, but she did not want Bruce to know. She tried to appear experienced.

Dick was a gentle, low-spirited horse and he hardly needed any reins, so Bruce handed them to Myra who seemed to want something to hold.

Beside a calm stretch of the river Bruce found a patch of cushiony white clover hidden from the road, but in view of the placid water where a feeding trout now and then jumped up after a winged insect, leaving silent ringlets spreading on the surface. Bruce laid the lap robe out and went in search of wood for a fire.

Myra opened her basket and took from it a blue and white damask tablecloth which she spread on the robe. A plate of fried spring chicken, a dish of potato salad and a saucer of assorted pickles soon appeared on it. But that was not all. She had made a small, three-layer yellow cake, deeply bedded in coconut frosting that oozed out all around it. Also in Myra's basket was a stone bottle full of hot coffee. It was the kind of supper Bruce had missed so much while boarding at the City Cafe. He got the seat cushion and placed it beside the picnic spread.

"There, Myra, that makes a good seat for you. I'll sit over there on the edge of the lap robe."

"Bruce, you found a perfect place for our picnic. It's so beautiful and restful here. My professor would call it a 'leafy arbor.' And we can watch the river out there almost washing our feet."

"Well, Myra, that river has nothing to compare with what I see here to eat. How do you do it? I thought you were just a boarding kind of schoolteacher, and not the best cook in Ellensburg already. If it tastes as good as it looks, there won't be any of it left here for those poor birds. I can tell you that!"

Myra smiled down at the heaping dishes. "Help yourself to the fried chicken, Bruce. I'll dish up some potato salad for us. I hope you enjoy it. I have already enjoyed getting it ready to bring."

"That kind of enjoyment is for you, Myra, but this fried chicken is for me. And I'm sure glad you enjoyed bringing this potato salad, too. Umm! No more City Cafe for me. After this, I couldn't swallow it."

"In this tray," Myra invited, "are olives, sweet pickles and little pickled beets. Auntie made the piccalilli in that jar."

For almost half an hour, their fascination with the picnic dishes made Bruce and Myra unconscious of the strained positions they were sitting in with their legs crossed. After that, there was hardly a bite left of all the culinary delights Myra had brought from home, except that the cake was still intact.

"Now are you ready for some cake, Mr. Bruce Calkins?"

"Listen, Myra. That 'mister' is flattering, but it doesn't do a thing to make room for any part of that delicious-looking cake. Just let me snooze here for an hour, and then I'll be able to tackle it."

"Oh, is that so! Then I'll quit honoring you with the title of 'mister.' But perhaps an intermission without sleep at this point might restore some portion of your appetite. Are you willing to try to stay awake someway, Bruce?"

"Well, that wouldn't be the hardest thing I've ever done, Myra. Not here with you on an evening like this, it wouldn't be. So let's leave the dishes the way they are and go watch the river while the fish are still jumping."

When Bruce reached his hand out to her, Myra put her hand in his. The air was warm and fragrant, the light was fading, and it was thrilling, walking hand in hand a little way to the riverbank. She was glad Bruce did not seem to know how much she liked his hand touching hers. It brought home to her how lonely she'd been. That was all in the past now. Anyway, it seemed that way because this evening Myra was incapable of knowing how true were those four little words the daughter of a Baghdad ruler had submitted as suitable for engraving inside a ring: "This, too, will pass."

There was a carpet of white clover on the riverbank. From it, an easy slope of sand and soil mixed with pebbles ran nearly to the water. While sitting on the clover-covered ledge, they could let their legs and feet rest at a comfortable angle on the slope. Bruce put his arm around Myra and helped her to sit down. Then, while she urged down her pink and white gingham dress, until its hem nearly reached her shoes, he got seated close beside her, casually taking her hand again.

"Now this is something, Myra! Are you glad you came?"

"Yes. Here I have lived in Ellensburg since I was twelve but never knew there was such a place as this so near me all that time."

"Well, these refreshments do a lot for it," Bruce said. "Now this. There! See that trout jump? He must a been a foot long. Too bad we don't have our fishing tackle."

"I would rather watch fish than catch them," Myra announced quietly.

"Yes, but if we'd been Indians living here, you'd caught them for a living."

"Of course. Although it would have hurt me to end their lives that way. But God meant for Indians to live on the fish. I just fail to see how it can be fun, as so many claim it is, to jerk a wiggling fish out of his home by a hook you have fooled him into thinking is good to eat, until he gets it barbed into his jaw. What makes anyone think that is fun, or sport either? Of course, those who like so much to lure the poor fish to their deaths are so sick of cleaning and eating them that they have to find some neighbor, such as the minister's daughter, willing to clean and cook their proud catch to keep it from going to waste. And while doing the job, to keep in mind with gratitude the brave skill that made it all possible. Do you think it's fun to catch fish, Bruce?"

"Not anymore I don't, Myra. Say, you can talk when you get started. But how come you know all that about fishing, right off the reel?"

"Oh, think nothing of it. In school I wrote something titled 'Fishing for Fun,' and that was the theme of it so I was ready for you. I know it's not fair. Now you tell me anything you have ready to say. Can you quote any Shakespeare?"

"Well, Myra, let's see, we had to memorize some Shakespeare. There was one that went, 'To be or not to be, that is the question whether' — no, it wasn't quite that way, let me think here."

"I think that is nice," Myra consoled him. "What other ones do you remember from Shakespeare?"

"Now I remember one. It went like this, 'Drink to me only with thine eyes, Juliet, tu . . . ta, tu . . . ta, tu . . . ta.' Somehow I don't seem to remember the next line."

"What other Shakespeare do you know?" Myra asked, turning her head to look up the river.

"I know a lot more, but I can't get my mind on him right now. Say, Myra, where you going to teach school this year? Do you know yet?"

"Upper Taneum, maybe. It is open, so I applied."

"You mean in that little dinky school up there on the creek?"

"I'm afraid so. I didn't want to go too far away from Ellensburg."

"That seems a long way up there to me. There sure isn't any train that goes there."

"I know it. I shall need a horse and buggy to go the fifteen miles. The problem is to get one."

"Yeah, and here I don't even have one I can lend you. I guess I'll have to buy one so I can take you and bring you back. We'll need a sleigh at Christmas. The snow gets deep up there."

"Bruce, how can you think of snow anywhere, it is so lovely here now. However, the moon coming up over there does look almost as white as snow."

"Yes, it does. Have you ever seen the man in the moon, Myra?"

"Why, of course. In a little while, maybe we shall see him there. And he shall be seeing us, I believe."

"Hear that *pflugg* out there on the water, Myra? The trout are still jumping. See those ripples that one made? They'll be in bed by the time the moon begins shining out there on the water. I wish we had a canoe and could paddle out there and maybe see the sleeping trout by the shine of the moon."

"Oh, Bruce, you sound like a poet. I like it right here on this riverbank with the moon coming out to give us company. It is too bad the trout who live in the water cannot smell, as I do, how sweet the new-mown hay is this summer evening. Its fragrance is everywhere. It may be in the water, too. I think it's wonderful you found this place, Bruce."

"I'm sure glad we found it. The river is smooth here,

but it's a roaring rapids going into the canyon down below there."

As Myra's gaze moved down the river toward the rapids, Bruce put her right hand into his and slowly, hesitantly, put his left arm around her.

"How do you like it here on the river, Myra?" Bruce asked quietly.

"Just fine," Myra said softly.

It was so romantic having Bruce close to her on this breath-of-heaven evening under a sky beginning to fill with the brightest stars. They were up there all the time, Myra thought to herself.

"There is something about you, Myra, that's better. Lots of Normal girls come to the drugstore, but they don't have — what is it? — the freshness or plain goodness you've got. It's what brought me to see you at church that morning."

"Oh, Bruce," Myra corrected him, "you don't mean that." But she prayed he did.

"Never meant anything more, Myra. Being with you makes me feel a lot less great than I've wished I was."

"Oh, piffle with that," Myra objected, as she pressed Bruce's hand a little and leaned more toward him. "You are at least as great as I am. I don't think either one of us wants to be great, do we? Only good. It is great, though, to be here listening to the song of the river rapids and to watch the moon seeming to rest on almost a solid bed of brightest stars, near enough to touch."

Myra's head was on Bruce's shoulder with her hair lightly caressing his face. She looked up at him and to the stars straight overhead, feeling very comfortable and cared for.

Bruce guessed that Myra had not gone out with boys. There were plenty of girls at the Normal who made it easier to be asked out than she had. There were few young men students there, so young men living in Ellensburg were lucky. Myra had always been attractive to him, but she was little more than nineteen. Myra thought he'd just discovered this secluded spot by the river. The truth was that on other evenings he'd come under the spell of the stars and the moon here more than once. As much as he wanted to tell all of that to Myra now, he wanted more to keep her, so he wouldn't dare tell.

Bruce looked into Myra's face and saw the light reflected from her dark eyes as she gazed toward the stars with a trace of a smile. Strands of hair were strewn over her forehead so invitingly that Bruce leaned over and gently pressed his lips on them. Myra did not turn her head but pressed Bruce's hand the least bit more. Myra seemed so purely innocent and trusting and good. She made him think of his sister at home, younger than Myra, and of how he hoped any man would respect her. It would be better to kiss Myra again and take her home.

Since Dick knew the way home to his oats and hay, Bruce looped the reins over the dashboard and put his arm around Myra's shoulder. She happily snuggled up close to him. In the buggy, it was quite as romantic as it had been back there on the riverbank. The moon and all the stars and even the summery smell of curing hay were still with them. But best of all, Bruce held her hand next to him.

"You know, Myra, I wish every evening was like this one."

"So do I," Myra breathed.

"Does this make you late getting home?"

"Not a bit. Papa knew I was going with you and he thinks you are fine."

"Well, I couldn't get a better recommendation than that."

"Now, I just thought of something, Bruce. Will you come to prayer meeting tomorrow evening?" Myra asked hopefully.

"There's no keeping me away, if you're going to be there," Bruce assured her.

Myra thought this a good sign, for if he were to come to prayer meeting Thursday evening, he would surely come to church Sunday morning. She replied, "I am at prayer meeting every Thursday evening."

"Well, Myra, my boss being a good Christian means my going to prayer meeting should set well with him. You never know, he might give me a raise."

"Yes, Bruce, Christians do get their reward, but it is one beyond compare with any number of raises in money."

"Myra, after this I couldn't deny that. Is the prayer meeting in the church?"

"Yes it is, but not so many come to it as come to the Sunday church services. Not nearly."

"You live so near the church, it leaves no distance to walk home with you after the meeting. But I know. We could walk over to Andy's Ice Cream Parlor and have a sundae afterward."

"That sounds to me like a good idea, Mr. Calkins."

"Yes, Miss Love, I expect it's the best idea I've had since I racked my brain to come up with the idea of hiring old Dick to haul us to our picnic this charming, summer evening."

"You shouldn't ought to do that, Bruce. You could rack and ruin your brain that way. Just the same, it was a lovely idea. But I wonder how good old Dick there feels about it."

"There's no telling that. And he's not talking on the job. After he's done, I'll speak to him at the livery stable and see how he felt about it. But I know he didn't have to worry much about flies this evening."

"How do you know that? I couldn't tell that you were slighting me anytime. So how could you see that old Dick was able to swish off those flies that wanted to dine on him?"

"Oh that's easy, Myra. I'm like you will have to be when you're at the blackboard up there on the Taneum, trying to teach those harum-scarum mountain kids something. You'll need eyes in the back of your head, just like the ones I watched old Dick with this evening."

"Oh, I already have eyes in the back of my head, as any misbehaving children in my school find out. I have had training as a teacher. As for old Dick, I am glad you saw he was not bothered much with hungry flies. He was so willing to take us out this evening."

"Myra," Bruce whispered, "this has been a wonderful evening. When can we have another one?"

"Never too soon for me," Myra whispered back. "Too bad that here already is where I live. So good night, Bruce."

"Good night, Myra. But let me help you down and walk to the door with you."

While Myra was going up to her room, Bruce sat in the buggy with his eyes on her open window. In the room she lit the lamp, then came to the window and waved at him as she pulled down the shade. When she moved around getting ready for bed, Bruce could sometimes see her shadow on the window shade. Dick tried to go, but Bruce checked him with the reins, until the light in the window went out.

Myra knelt at her bed and prayed for a longer time than usual. Then, in bed she could not sleep. She wondered why Bruce's reddish hair, blue eyes and freckles had such an appeal for her, when her own eyes and hair were so dark, like her mother's had been she was told.

"Oh," she said to herself, "that is it. Papa's hair was red and his eyebrows still are. And his eyes are blue, too. It comes natural. But I never thought anyone could be as nice as Papa is to me — in a different way. The smell of the air here is quite as sweet as it was out there on the river, and still has the essence of new-mown hay a little in it — or do I imagine that? It was like paradise there with Bruce. He surely likes me all I could want and his tenderness to me nearly carried me away through the air. It would have, if there were any way for people to go through the air. But I didn't want to go through the air. I wanted only to breathe it there with him — and I do now. There are no words for such a feeling. I am grateful to God for His blessing this evening and will try my best to show I may have deserved it — but how could I? Just to think — out there under the moon — a summer moon — and those million stars in the sky, with the murmur of the river rapids round the bend, in the dead still night, and a fine . . . and a fi . . . . ''

Myra went to sleep. She'd wanted to stay awake with her dream, but perhaps it would be sweeter asleep. She did not sleep long though. When she opened her eyes, the night had only begun to retreat before the early summer dawn. But she wanted to be awake and delight in the rapture she felt. She wondered whether Bruce also had been wakened in the hushed gray dawn. Was he still under the spell of the summer evening, like she was? He was a gentleman. He'd shown how fine he was and would be. She had prayed to have a friend like him. And to think, he would come to prayer meeting, too. It made her feel so good thinking of him. He might want to marry her, and she hoped he would. Not that she wanted to get married soon because she intended to teach for a while, but if Bruce always cared for her as much as she wanted him to, he would wait. That was the only way to know.

Summers have a way of going fast, especially for lovers. Myra and Bruce would gladly have kept forever the summer in which they had met, but it fled on toward September, seeming to gain speed with each passing day. On many evenings they went for long walks and on the way back to Myra's home found refreshment at Andy's Ice Cream Parlor.

Socials were held in the church hall occasionally, and Myra
and Bruce attended them whether for young or old. Everyone there thought them a fine-looking couple. Whenever
Myra was in church Bruce was there, and on the twentieth
of August he was baptized by her father and formally re-
ceived into the fellowship of the church. That was a happy
day in Myra's life, to have helped bring one so dear to her
into the fold. Her father and Auntie were happy, too.

When the time came for Myra to go to her school, it was
a problem for Bruce to get days off at the drugstore so he
could drive her up the Taneum. But finally he was given
the two days needed for the round trip. Myra would open
the school on Tuesday following Labor Day. At the close of
church on the last Sunday morning of their summer, Bruce
and Myra were ready to go. Bruce had Dick at the side door.

Myra's father and aunt came out to bid her good-bye.
She kissed them both, but words came hard now that she was
leaving home for the first time. She stepped up and sat down
beside Bruce on the buggy seat.

"I see my trunk in back of us," she said casually. "I shall
need it up there."

"Yes, Myra, I am sure you will," Bruce said. "That parasol will be needed today, too. The sun is shining good. Oh,
wait a minute, I almost forgot. There is a big canvas umbrella folded up down there on the floor. A bracket on this
seat will hold it up straight between us, so we won't have to
hold it. It will sure keep that sun off us. Your parasol,
though, will help when the sun gets down below the umbrella. You stay right where you are, Myra. I will put it up
while you visit with your father and aunt. . . . There, it is in
place, good as a roof over us. Of course, we will be advertising plows, rakes, bolts, nails and pails for Pease Hardware
Company in big letters on it. But that won't let the hot sun
get through. The settlers up on the Taneum, who can read,

will see where they can get things like a milk pail or some tenpenny nails — after a fifteen mile drive, that is. Sure glad that wind isn't blowing like it does blow some days. Cluck-cluck, giddap, Dick."

"Good-bye, Papa and Auntie," Myra called as Dick trotted away. "Bruce, isn't it a nice day for traveling? This umbrella is so interesting and cozy to be under. Your driving me up there is too much, and this umbrella will make me want to come back with you. I do anyway. Oh well, it is time for me to get out into the world and do some good with the education given me at normal school."

"Oh, you will do good with it, Myra. Where did you say you were going to board and room?"

"At Yendees'. They have a daughter, Rebecca, who will be my only eighth grader. Mrs. Southern, her teacher last year, told me she is a good scholar. Teaching her more than she already knows may be a severe task. But Mr. and Mrs. Yendee spent very little time in school, so perhaps I shall be able to amaze them a little with my reading, writing and arithmetic. Teaching a school lost deep in some canyon like the Taneum is where you get an opportunity like that."

"Yes, Myra, that solves the mystery of your wanting to teach up on the Taneum. You never know, there could be other parents around there — if not their children — for you to amaze."

"Well," Myra laughed, "I should be satisfied only to see Mr. and Mrs. Yendee gasp now and then when they begin to notice how much I learned at normal school."

"Yes, that could help to while away some long winter evenings. We are coming to the river bridge. Over there a ways is where we had our first picnic."

"It would be nice to see it again," Myra sighed.

"No spot on the river like it, is there, Myra? But today I'm afraid Dick has all he can do to get us up there to your school. This loaded buggy is a little heavy for him to pull in all this heat. If old Dick should play out, I might have to get down between the shafts myself while he builds his strength in some pasture along the road."

"Well, if there is any danger of that, Bruce, we had better get you fed beforehand. Is there any place along here where we can pause long enough for you to gain some strength from this lunch I knew I had better bring along?"

"Of course there is, Myra. I knew you wouldn't want me straining down there between those shafts without strength enough to pull this rig — so I thought I'd mention it to you. It happens that just across the bridge, along that steep high bank, is a spring of clear, cold water. A bench and a bucket used to be there. And there were tin cans to drink the water from — rusty ones. Dick can drink from the bucket and munch grass near the spring, while we are living high on the hog out of that basket I see you brought."

As usual, Myra had brought a basket lunch, and as usual Bruce could hardly wait until she would let him at it. He could never get enough of her fried chicken and layer cake. And now today they had the coolest and sweetest water to drink ever sprung out of the ground. The one rusty tin can for both to drink from made it taste even sweeter. After lunch they wanted to stay in the shade by the spring, but they had to get back on the road. There were a dozen miles still to go.

The first few miles had been a smoother and straighter stretch of road than the one Dick had yet to take Bruce and Myra over. It would get rockier in places, more up and down, curved and narrow. But hand in hand sometimes — always on the cushioned comfort of the seat and hidden from the sun under the buggy-wide, friendly umbrella — Bruce and Myra found a portion of their happiness that day, as oblivious to bumps they sang hymns long familiar to her and becoming familiar to him.

They sang between farmhouses. When near them, it was interesting to observe the houses and nearby barns, or watch the horses and cows, maybe a bull. There were also sheep and pigs they could see grazing now and then in the meadows lately harvested.

"That road goes down to Thorp, Myra."

"Yes. I have been there on the train to attend an evening service that Papa preached for. I wanted to teach there, but they had no vacancy this year. So now it's up the Taneum we go."

"Oh well, Myra, it's better to start up high, then it's easy to come down."

"Did you read that in a book, Bruce?"

"It's in one I wrote. The others tell you to start out low, but I've figured it out. It's harder to get up high when you start low. Just supposing you were starting out clear down there at Thorp. You'd be in a rut you couldn't get out of, so you'd never get to be high up on the Taneum. See what I mean, Myra?"

"Well . . . no . . . not exactly. Perhaps I shall have to read your book before I know your full meaning. Did you bring it with you?"

"As a matter of fact the publishers haven't sent me any copy. As soon as they send it, you will be next after me to read it."

"I thought you wrote it. Why do you have to read it?"

"Well, Myra, if you've never written a book, you can't imagine how many ideas you have to have in one. I put so many in the one I wrote, I couldn't begin to remember them all. So like anyone else, I have to read the book to know what's in it."

"Not very often, I hope. Now I see a few tombstones inside of that fence."

"Yes, there are. I happen to know that cemetery was plotted there by the Odd Fellows Lodge of Thorp. Somebody had to do it."

"Of course. There are many people living up in this part of the valley, and that is where their mortal remains may sadly be brought by their loved ones. Our Christian faith, though, assures us that is not the end, but only the beginning of real happiness. Bruce, is this near where you lived on a farm one time?"

"It sure is. See that big white house back up there, maybe a quarter of a mile? It was built after we moved away. The smaller unpainted house off to the right of it is where we lived. Right ahead of us is the schoolhouse I was in for eight years."

"Eight years? Then where did you go?"

"We moved to Olympia, and I got in high school there when I was fourteen."

"No wonder you are so smart. Did you learn much going to the little school here?"

"Quite a bit, although there were only two teachers in the whole school. For the first four years I had Miss Page. When she got done with you, you had a pretty fair education in a lot of things without ever going to school again. Then they closed the school in this place, and she moved to Thorp after I left."

"Was Miss Page strict?"

"Worse than that! Be sure after she had tanned you for not knowing your lesson, you would know it a lot better the next time."

"Then that is how you got smart enough to go to high school — even college? How did your father and mother like Miss Page?"

"That was the trouble. I didn't dare tell them Miss Page gave me a tanning, or you know, there'd probably be another one at home."

"That is very interesting to a teacher who is starting out up here, as you say, 'at the top.' "

"I thought it would be. For another thing, this trip is giving me a good chance to let you know how great I am. I never told you that before, did I?" Bruce spoke as though wondering, while giving Myra a gentle hug.

"No, but you sort of hinted around at it," she murmured as she leaned her head on his shoulder. Both softly giggled.

"You can see the railroad over there, Myra, and the bridge it crosses the river on."

"Yes, there is a train running on it at noon that I hope to come home on sometimes. But how will I get back to school in time?"

"We will have to get you back someway, Myra. The trouble is that I can't always get time off at the drugstore. But what worries me right now is whether old Dick can last all the way up the Taneum to your school. The going keeps getting harder. There's a place for him to get a drink not far from here. Wish we had an umbrella for him. We haven't met many rigs on the road today. But there is one coming now and, sure enough, it's Nigger Evans driving a roan and a buckskin to his buggy. He won't hurt you!"

"Nigger Evans? Why do you call him 'Nigger'?"

"I don't know. Everyone calls him that — because he's colored. Probably used to be a slave. They called him that. He's used to it. But if you want me to, I'll call him 'Mr. Evans.' "

"Yes, I think that would be nicer. We are out here where we need friendly people."

"Here he is. . . . Howdy, Mr. Evans. I'm Bruce. Remember?"

"Why sho I do. You used ter live on de ol Calkins place. Wha you all headin fo?"

"Miss Love here is the teacher at the upper Taneum school this term. Got to get her up there because school's beginning."

"Oh sho. Hot day fo drivin, ain't it? Yo lucky you got er umbreller."

"Yeah, Mr. Evans, that's for selling nails, rakes, bolts or buckets. 'Come to Pease,' it says. Good-bye, Mr. Evans."

"Bye, yo all. Giddap!"

"Now isn't that better than calling him 'Nigger Evans'?" Myra asked.

"I suppose so. But I always thought of him being Nigger Evans about like you would think of someone being Red Jones or Slim Brown. I never connected him with nigger-town out there across the railroad tracks. Not with a farm up here like he's got."

"I am glad that Mr. Evans seemed to enjoy meeting us. How many miles do we have to go, Bruce?"

"Probably four, over a narrow canyon road. But first we have to cross this bridge over the Taneum, near its mouth. The farmers from Thorp Prairie come down here with barrels on their wagons and dip water out of this creek to haul home. There's one now. See him? Oh, I know him. It's Dobie Shaw. While Dick is drinking, Dobie will want to jaw some with us to give him a chance to meet the new school ma'am who's going to be up the canyon. He knows them all up there, and they know him. He's so busy dipping that water, he doesn't know we're here yet. Yoo-hoo! Dobie!"

With his bucket still full of water, Dobie turned around until he saw Bruce and Myra sitting in their buggy.

"Well, I'll be dinged if you ain't little Bruce, Burt Calkins's boy." Dobie set his bucket down and came walking toward the buggy.

"That's me. Mr. Dobie Shaw, this is Miss Myra Love, who is brave enough to be the teacher way up in the Taneum."

"It is a pleasure to meet you, Mr. Shaw."

Dobie took off his battered straw hat as he turned and squirted a stream of tobacco juice through the part in his heavy mustache onto the hot rocks at the dry edge of the creek bed.

"Yes, mom, it's a pleasure meetin you likewise. You'll find room up there with Hattie, my oldest sister. She married Rube Yendee. Lives a short walk t'other side of the schoolhouse."

"Oh, is she your sister? I have made arrangements to stay with Mrs. Yendee. I will tell her I saw you."

"Then she'll be watchin for you. She always keeps the school ma'am, so I reckon she'll be plumb proud to keep you. Bruce here's turned out good, ain't he? I seen him down there workin in the drugstore. That sure beats havin to haul water so as to keep you alive in this heat. It's good you're fit'n fine, cause I hear them kids up the creek are fixin to aggrivate the new teacher. Did you fetch yourself a hickory?"

"Why . . . no. I never knew any hickory grew in this valley. Other things do, though. It's thoughtful of you to give me warning, Mr. Shaw. But I enjoy my work with children. Come and see us."

"Well, Dobie, I guess we'd better be pushing on. I'll be looking to see you in the drugstore again. So long."

"Good luck, Bruce, and you too, ma'am. Be sure you get some drinkin water out of that spring about a hundred yards on up."

"Thanks, Dobie," Bruce replied.

He and Myra quenched their thirsts at the spring and soon were rolling on the narrow road above the creek.

"Well, Bruce, from the looks of this stream we are following, I shall not have to haul my water from back there like Mr. Shaw does. At least I can be thankful for that."

"That's true, Myra. The road forked back there. Dobie will take the right fork up through that shallow, dry canyon and farther on to his farm on the prairie where the cold wind blows all spring — strong enough to pull the feathers off a sage hen. The sun is hot enough there in summer to drive cold-blooded rattlesnakes from the prairie clear down to that creek. Of course, a horse left up there in the winter would freeze to death, so they move them over to the Taneum as soon as cold weather sets in. But it's real tolerable up there sometimes in the autumn — if you don't run out of water unexpectedly."

"Then, Mr. Calkins, we are all the more obliged to the hardy folks struggling up on that prairie, making it possible for us who work in nice warm schoolhouses and drugstores to have potatoes and wheat to eat and all the clear cool water we can drink. I am sorry now we did not let Mr. Shaw know how grateful we should feel to him."

"But, Myra, we didn't compel or so much as ask Dobie and his neighbors to move onto the prairie. Being there looked like the best they could do. But today we are taking the left fork of the road on the trail of those certain other homesteaders to whom plenty of water and wood and a few acres of green bottom land looked better than a hundred and sixty acres of dry wheat land up on the prairie. Wait — look over there by the creek. I swan if that isn't Asa Yerkes resting his back against that cottonwood. In the store not long ago he said he was still living up in Rattlesnake Canyon. Whoa, Dick. Maybe he wants a ride."

Asa looked to be napping until, tilting his bald head back

against the tree, he raised his arm and waved at Bruce and Myra. Then he covered his head with a brown canvas, floppy-brimmed and shapeless-crowned hat, and with some effort stood up. It was a steep climb to the buggy and Asa was short-legged and too stout around the middle, but with some puffing he made it. His eyes were dark with heavy brows to match, and his iron-gray whiskers were many weeks long. Myra and Bruce saw that his woolen checked-gray pants, frayed at the bottom, were held up by sweat-stained wide elastic suspenders. The collar of his brown plaid shirt was unbuttoned and so were his sleeves, all revealing soiled edges of heavy red woolen underwear. It was a hot day, but Asa believed that what would keep out cold would keep out heat.

"Where you headin for, Mr. Yerkes? Want a lift?" Bruce asked.

"Hush up that 'mister' business. I'm Asa. Yeah, I reckon I'll ride with yuh. Goin up to Felix's, my brother's. Tain't fur. I'll stand up thar ahind the seat and chin with yuh. Hang onto them reins . . . now I'm in. You kin loosen the brakes." There was a nasal ring in Asa's loud voice.

After folding down the umbrella to make headroom, Bruce introduced Mr. Yerkes to Miss Love.

"Giddap, Dick! Tluck, tluck. Asa, how d'you like livin down near this Taneum water?"

"Ain't so much of it this time a year. My spring comes dang nigh to toppin it. I got a trail up over the hill thar fur a couple a miles goin to it."

"Asa, I wonder why you didn't settle along this creek in the early days like Felix did?"

"Yeah, me too. I was in here ahead of him. But I heerd bout this spring all by its lonesome up in that lost canyon. I give it the name 'Rattlesnake.' "

"Why'd you call it that, Asa?"

"I mind now what give me the idea was ever time I clomped tolable hard on the kitchen deckin, them rattlers beneath'd start stirrin up a fuss."

"Gee! Is that a fact?"

"Yep. Thar weren't no fear a nosybodies movin in on me. Soon es Felix and Zeke come follerin me out here with a woman apiece, sides some young'ns, I showed em up the Taneum, but Zeke tarned round'n homestidded a quarter section on the prairie. You might a seen him dippin water back thar. Some yars he makes a livin off a nothin cept wheat'n spuds — thout no water even."

"How does Felix do down here on the creek?"

"Fairly tolable. He kin catch hisself a dozen trout er two in case the folks is starvin. That creek bottom shorely grows the finest a roots an berries thar is. Havin a fat buck handy to hang in your smokehut now and then ain't no hardship nuther. Leastwise not on top a all the cheese'n butter yuh kin want. Kate raises eggs nough to feed a thrashin crew, and Felix sells a few sawlogs down to the mill, when he's a mind to, or mebbe some cordwood to them what's a needin fuel."

"That sure sounds like living, doesn't it, Myra?"

"Yes, it certainly does."

"How d'you like it up in Rattlesnake, Asa?"

"Good es any, I reckon. In case thar ain't nough crop f'rinstance, I rustle me up a balky horse not worth nothin but lookin smooth and perk es a bantie rooster. Gittin him traded off to one a them Philadelphia lawyers down at the Burg keeps the dang wolf from the door — even in a thirty-below winter. Heh, heh, heh!"

"Yeah, I know how it is, Asa. Those slickers down at the Burg will trust an honest farmer like you in a trade any day."

"Uh, huh! Heh, heh, heh, heh! They's more'n one ways

a skinnin a cat. Huh, huh, huh, huh!" Even Myra could not keep from joining in Asa's hearty laugh.

"Speaking of a wolf, are you ever bothered up there by them? Or by cougars?"

"Plenty a times. But back in thar's whar Felix lives. Gotta git off here." Bruce stopped Dick, and Asa climbed down. When on the ground, he turned and faced Myra and Bruce, curling his fingers around the top of the buggy wheel rim. His dark eyes glowed up at them.

"Now, speakin a cougars botherin yuh. Genrally they don't. But this'n got makin hisself a nuisance. Like one night, I were sleepin dog-tired and, it bein August, had the winder wide open. All a sudden I felt a kind a jar. Woke me up, yuh know. Felt somethin heavy on my legs. So I looks down an dang me if thar weren't a pair a big shiny eyes starin direct through me. So I says to myself, says I, 'Asa, yuh got company. More'n likely a cougar.' Anyways I knowed I has to stare him down or I'm a goner. An danged me that time it worked. That cougar got to thinkin he'd best leave. So he gits up and gins crawlin back out through the winder. I'm purty mad, yuh know, bein woke up and distarbed that way, so I catched at his hind ankles. In them days, yuh know, I were stout es a yoked-young bull, so I slung that cougar ahind me, back to back. He jest couldn't do nothin cept squirm and howl. Packed him out to the waterin trough and ducked him till he were drowned deader'n a rattler's lost skin. That were a warnin to all the rest of them thar cougars." Asa's eyes were all aglow as he gazed at Myra and Bruce in expectation of the moving effect his story would have on them. Then satisfied, he said, "Much obliged. Good luck to ye, ma'am," and turning, Asa walked down the lane toward the creek.

"Asa's quite a storyteller, isn't he, Myra?"

"Yes, but he almost makes me wish I were coming up here to homestead rather than to teach school."

"Well, if you do decide on a homestead, try to find one on that side, the south side of the creek. This side we're on is where the rattlers all stay so as to be in the sun. They go down to the creek, but they don't cross it. Look ahead there, quick! One is sneaking across the road now. Looks pretty big, too. Whoa, Dick! Let him get out of our way."

"Oh mercy! I never thought of this canyon being infested with rattlesnakes."

"Not really infested, Myra. Just a pair of them here and there. Except when they're denned up for winter. Then I'd hate to have to count them all."

"Yes, I wonder who would not," Myra said wryly. "Well, life seems to go on up here, rattlesnakes or no. I am sure there is a way to avoid them."

"Mr. and Mrs. Yendee will be able to tell you how to do that better than I can. The cougars up in here are not apt to bother you any. The black bears may leave you alone, too."

"Yes they may, for it seems I shall be sure to stay pretty close to the Yendees', when I am not in the schoolhouse. I did not come up here to meet cougars, bears or rattlesnakes. But tell me. How narrow and steep does this road get? Old Dick there hardly has room to walk, and I look almost straight down on my side to I don't know where. I don't like this."

"It looks plenty solid over here on my side, Myra, just a rattlesnake hole once in a while. There's a few other steep places on the road something like this, but old Dick is sure-footed. There's nothing to worry about. The folks on the Taneum can't afford enough taxes for the county to build them a decent road."

"Then for pity's sake, why can't those people in the valley who have decent roads pitch in up here and build a road on which these people would not have to risk their lives every time they went out to trade? Answer me that, Bruce."

"Well, Myra, it's hard to say. But first of all, maybe these canyon folks would rather keep the kind of road their valley neighbors would just as soon stay off of. A safe and easy road up here would bring in many wanting to clean the trout out of the creek and kill animals and birds just for fun. They'd contaminate the water, steal the crops and clutter up the creek bank from end to end with their picnic trash. Some would even buy creek land up here and fence it in."

"That's enough, Mr. Calkins. Miss Love will bear with the road just the way it is. Now I see one reason why these creek people might want the rattlesnakes to live on their property. The very name *rattlesnake* could give pause to many who would make themselves worse than a nuisance, were there not a few of those snakes along this road. And they may be why the residents here leave this trail-wide road in its rocky, up-and-down, mountainside state. But it takes an abiding sense of Christian duty to make me continue on the road, even though I have you beside me, Bruce. It is only too evident that during this term I shall not be home very often to attend Sunday morning services."

"No, Myra, it wouldn't be safe for you to travel down there by yourself, and you'll find it seldom anyone up here drives to Thorp. But you may be able to hold a Sunday service in the schoolhouse. I know you told me that Suzanna Wesley, whom you greatly admire, taught others from the Bible."

"Yes, that is an idea. I hope there is an organ or a piano in the school. Somehow I will bring these folks in there and get them to sing 'What a Friend We Have in Jesus.' Oh my! Now we're in the shade of these nice trees."

"Yes," Bruce said. "Now the road drops down to the

floor of the canyon. It'll be cooler there along the creek. We'll fold up this umbrella so's we can see around better."

"Well, this seems to me to have the typical features of a canyon — deep, steep and narrow bare rock walls on one side and trees, tall and dark, crowding the other. But why not call it the Taneum Gash? It opens like a gash into the mountain body. But in the schoolroom I will keep in mind that this is a canyon."

"Myra, whatever you call it, I like fine. Old Dick there feels the same. He is getting tired and no wonder. We can stop ahead there in the shade and let him rest a few minutes. Now he must have heard that. . . . See, he's taking off on a trot to get into that shade. It's going to be pretty lonesome on this road tomorrow. Just him and me."

"Imagine what it will be like for me. I don't expect to be invited out for dinner. If you have never been missed before, Bruce, you may rest assured you will be missed tomorrow. But this is nice. Just look at that grand old tree, half as tall as the sky, with its thick coat the color of chestnut dappled with black."

"That's an old pine, if there ever was one," Bruce said. "We'll stop ahead there in the shade of those willows, where it's hard for a rattlesnake to hide. Whoa, Dick! Take a rest now."

"Bruce, how old do you think that tree is?"

"No way of telling, but I guess it had its roots put down there before the morning Columbus weighed anchors to begin his westward journey. That was four hundred years ago."

"Just think of that. I have read of trees being even older than that."

"Yes, Myra, there is a good chance that on the day Columbus set sail, an ancestor of these rattlers was around here enjoying the shade under the branches of that tree, a lot nearer to the ground then. But before Columbus ever saw the land again, the old ancestor was back up in his den above yonder granite wall. He was cuddled up with his relations or laying out on the rocks soaking up all the sun he could get. Just imagine, for over four hundred years, every year, some rattlers have laid under that very tree to cool off.

"But one of these mornings," Bruce continued, "perhaps while you are in this canyon, it's going to happen. A couple of hardened, sweating, tobacco-stained lumberjacks carrying a double-bitted axe apiece and a crosscut saw will come here. They will look at that tree, up to its top, and one will say, 'Well, what d'yuh know! Is that what we got to knock down?' And the other one will spit out a gob of tobacco juice and say, 'Lookit that knotty, pitch-seamed batch of timber. It's a towerin ol snag, ain't it?' But they will use some real strong cusswords. Then, in only a few hours, the tree that grew ring on ring, year by year, up into that sky for four long centuries, won't be up there anymore."

"That's terrible! To think that men would have no more respect for great age and magnificence than to destroy the noblest reminder of it without one reverent sign or word of thankfulness, and while using the vilest profanity they can lay their tongues to. I would hate to have to think that it was from a tree cursed by men that our church and parsonage were built."

"Myra, I hope you don't have to hear the kind of language some lumberjacks like to use, but in this canyon I'm afraid you will."

"Of course, Bruce, I understand. I am only glad that is not your kind of language."

Bruce pointed to the outcropped roots of a foot-thick willow tree about ten feet from the road. "There, Myra, is where young Calkins found himself about as near to a rattler as you could ever get without sitting down on him. Lucky he had his head end into a hole by that root thinking he was hid. Most of him was laying outside, but he sure blended in with the ground. It's a wonder I didn't put my hand or foot on him. It scares me now to see how close a call it was."

"I am glad it was not worse. What were you doing up here?"

"Oh, Pa was logging around the bend just ahead of us, and I was helping. It was the year we left the farm and moved to Everett."

"Then no wonder you are acquainted here."

"Well, Myra, we're on our way again. Right over there is where Oliver and Maude Cummins live. There's Oliver with his pail going out to milk the cows. And that's Maude gathering onions and stuff from the garden. See how neatly her hair is done up? She never had any fancy clothes but always looks like her cooking would be very good to eat. I wish we had time and the invitation now. We'll just have to wave at them this time. See that little log house? They live in it. Now look what's coming ahead there. It's Doc Wagner with his remedies."

Doc, wearing an ancient-looking Panama hat, was slouched on the worn seat of a light wagon. His thick, graying mustache was stained by puffing tobacco smoke from a brown meerschaum pipe now held in his mouth. The tongue of the hack sagged between two tired-looking buckskin horses. Reins in hand, Doc sat under a hood in front of a faded black van with the words WALKER'S REMEDIES painted on its sides. He stopped when Bruce and Myra drew alongside.

"Whoa, Dick. Remember me, Doc? I'm Bruce who used to live on the old Thomas place. This is Myra Love who'll be the teacher up here."

"Why, of course I remember you! Kept you in pills and liniments for years. That's how he got growed up, ma'am,"

Doc said, as he gave Myra a wink. "Hattie is looking for you up there. She told me so. Fine woman Hattie is, too. You'll get to know. I just spent a hour with her and Rube."

"Thank you, Mr. Wagner," Myra said. "I am looking forward to seeing the Yendees, very soon I hope. Perhaps I shall see you on your next trip, Mr. Wagner."

"You'd have a hard time to keep from seeing me, ma'am. You'll be needing some remedy from me most likely. Besides, I carry perfumery face and hand powder for ladies. Our sweet pea smelling cold cream's extra cool and creamy feeling. When them kids give you a headache, I'll cure you of it with Walker's headache elixir. Keep it back there all the time."

"Thank you, Mr. Wagner, but I do not expect I shall need your headache cure."

"What you been working at, Bruce?" Doc asked.

"Well, Doc, I'm a druggist now, so if you're needing pills or liniment I'll fix you up at Young's Drug Store in Ellensburg, paying you back for all you did for me on the farm."

"Oh bushwah! You couldn't cure a blackhead with them kind of concoctions you're peddling. I'm the only one in the whole vicinity who's got a cure for consumption: 'Dr. Walker's Sure Cure for Consumption.' Guaranteed! Tom Gilman over there on the prairie had it bad. He just took six bottles of 'Cure' like it says on the directions. After that he growed the biggest crop of wheat on the prairie. But you have to take all six bottles, just like it says, or it won't work — go ask Tom. That reminds me," Doc added as he remembered something that made him laugh. "Come on back to my van door, and I'll let you see what the 'Cure' looks like, Bruce. I doubt the lady'd care to see it." Doc and Bruce got down and went to the rear of the van.

"Bruce, I just wanted to tell you this because maybe it's not what you tell ladies, or leastwise not school ma'ams.

Anyway, one day a while back I stopped over at Tom's place to see how he was making out — not expecting he needed anything. Well, sir, there he was out in the field, and danged me if he don't have a horse hitched up with his bull to a harrow. I noticed there was some horses running out in his pasture. So I says to Tom, I says, 'Tom, how come you got that bull hitched up working him so hard, all the time there's horses out loose over there doing nothing?' 'Well, Doc,' says he, never cracking a smile, 'I just want to show that big lazy brute there's somethin in this world besides pleasure.' "

Doc could hardly get his last words out for laughing and slapping Bruce on the shoulder and bending and spitting while tears came into his eyes. They both forgot about the consumption cure and returned, each to his seat.

"Well, Doc," Bruce said, "I'm glad we ran into you. Myra and I have to be going. What are you going to do?"

"Coming up this morning," Doc said, "I catched a fine mess of rainbows and left them there with Maude Cummins. She'll have them fried in that homemade butter of hers and tastier'n anything Queen Victoria ever puts her tongue next to, I can tell you. But the truth is, I mainly leave the trout with Maude so's I can get some apple pie when I come back for supper. The apples come fresh off them trees you can see there. What she does with them is more magical than any cure I know of. Here, ma'am, is a can of carbolic salve, compliments of old Doc. It's good for nearly anything. You'll read that in the directions on top a the can."

"Thank you again, Mr. Wagner, and good day."

"Good-bye, Doc. See you again."

"Good day to you, ma'am, and Bruce. Tell Rube and Hattie you seen me."

"Giddap, Dick! Cluck-cluck."

"Well, at least old Dick got a little rest there, Bruce. I

enjoyed meeting Mr. Wagner. What was so funny about a bottle of supposed consumption cure?"

"Oh, Doc had a yarn to tell me, and he could hardly tell it for laughing. He said he wouldn't tell it to a lady, especially a school ma'am. It shows the kind of respect these people have for their teacher. Now here we are on the bridge. From here on the road is on the south side of the creek, safe from rattlers."

"That sounds good. How far would you say it is to the Yendees', Bruce?"

"Oh, hardly two miles, mostly in the shade. Whoa, Dick. We'll just sit here and enjoy the smell of the timber and listen to the rippling creek over there racing down to join the river on its way to the ocean. Myra, how long would you guess it will take for that very water we see now to move out into the Pacific Ocean?"

"It might get there by the time we get to Yendees'," Myra laughed. "It must be awfully lonesome in the ocean with no trees for company. Too bad a creek has to leave a home like this. I know how lonesome *I* would feel, coming up here this evening without you, Bruce."

Bruce looped the reins over the dashboard, then put his arm around Myra's shoulder, and she moved closer to him. The last day of this summer they could spend together was coming swiftly to an end. Myra wondered whether Bruce felt as sad as she did. It had been the happiest summer of her life. Bruce turned his head toward her, and she turned her face up to him.

The wheels of the buggy began to roll on softly. Dick padded his hooves, two and two, on the cushiony dirt road. His rhythmic thuds blended with mellow sounds of leather tugs rubbing on singletree ends and wood buggy joints straining under their load, to compose a soothing faint-toned melody.

Myra turned her head to look at Dick as she quietly said, "He is such a fine horse — true and gentle. He has seemed to enjoy taking us up here. I hate to think of him being driven by thoughtless, demanding people as I am sure he must sometimes be."

"With your salary from teaching school this term, perhaps you could buy him, Myra."

"I surely would like to have him," Myra replied.

"And there is certainly nothing that would suit Dick more than belonging to you, Myra," Bruce whispered as he drew her even closer to him. "I know Dick must feel that way because nothing would suit me as much as belonging to you."

Myra turned her head slightly to look up at the tall virgin pines with their amber-colored bark and long green needles. A gray squirrel with a long bushy tail ran up one and disappeared. Her heart seemed to stand still, not certain Bruce's words meant all she wanted them to.

Her words came out slowly, quaveringly, "What do you mean, Bruce?"

"That I want you to marry me," Bruce said simply, with his eyes on Dick.

Myra lowered her head. Then, in a moment, she turned her face up to look into Bruce's eyes before she closed her own. It was not the time to talk. Their hearts were pounding with joy. . . .

"Oh, Myra," Bruce exclaimed, "look! There is your little one-room schoolhouse."

"Well, so it is," Myra chimed in. "And all painted red, too. It looks good to me."

"Yes," Bruce agreed. "See, there's a belfry with a bell you can ring."

"It surely is a neat little schoolhouse," Myra said happily. "There are two windows on this side. Just imagine how inviting it will look with smoke curling out of that chimney. I hope the children will think so. Oh, that must be Yendees' place we can see there now. It is an easy walk to the school. But I know the snow gets quite deep to walk in up here. There is someone coming out of the barn now and going toward the house. It must be Mr. Yendee."

"Well, Myra, we'll soon know who it is. We'll take that lane leading off the road to the house. It's not a log house like others up here — doesn't look like it's had any paint on it, though."

"Goodness me," Myra exclaimed, "it does not look very big for four people to live in. Now that must be Mrs. Yendee with Rebecca."

The three Yendees stood by their house ready to meet the new schoolteacher coming down the lane in the buggy. Mr. Yendee stepped over to Dick who was only too willing to stop and receive a few pats on his nose. Rebecca's dark eyes were directed toward Dick's feet. Her hair was in a long braid, and she wore a red calico dress which hung below her knees. Mrs. Yendee, lean and tall, with folded arms, peered up into Myra's face. Her dark hair, streaked with gray, was done up on top of her head. Her long apron and dress were made of mixed gray calico. Mrs. Yendee reminded Myra of the pioneer woman she had seen in a picture. Mr. Yendee was not as tall as his wife. His half-gray mustache flapped up and down, and his bright eyes sparkled as he laughed and talked to Dick. He wore a red calico print shirt with blue denim pants and a well-worn cap, and he looked at home on the Taneum.

"Be you the new school mom coming to board here?" Mrs. Yendee asked.

"Yes, Mrs. Yendee, I am Miss Love."

"Then I got room for yuh. You kin pay me twelve

dollars a month, soon as your warrant comes. Ain't that fair enough?"

"Of course it is fair, Mrs. Yendee."

"Then yuh might as well light down here and come on in. The menfolk kin fetch your trunk. I'll fix you some supper."

Myra got down from the buggy and walked around to where Mrs. Yendee waited.

"Him and you ain't hitched up, be you? They said you was an old maid, but you ain't that old from the way it looks. This be Becky. Her given name's Rebecca. She's mighty proud a bein the eighth grade this time. Me and her paw is likewise."

"Yes, you ought to be proud. How do you do, Rebecca. I am glad you will be in school with me."

Rebecca grinned and then ran inside the house as her mother and Myra followed. Mr. Yendee and Bruce took the trunk from in back of the buggy and carried it into a tiny bedroom at the front of the house. They both got into the buggy.

"Drive down to the barn, and we'll put your horse up. Hattie'll get yuh some supper," Mr. Yendee, or Rube, as Bruce soon called him, said. "Did you come clean from Ellensburg?"

"Yes, and old Dick is pretty tired and hungry, so he's glad to see this place. Getting to stop here for some water and hay will make him think he's found 'horse heaven' all the way up here on the Taneum. Some supper will look good to me, too, I can tell you."

"That trough's runnin over with clear water. Soon as Dick gits his fill a hit we'll tie him in Bill's stall. I got some oats fur Dick with timothy fresh out a the medder. Say, Bruce, what do ye call that thing under his tail?" Rube asked in a serious but somewhat squeaky voice.

"Oh that?" Bruce replied. "That's called a crupper."
Bruce wondered why Rube wouldn't know that.

Rube began to bend and laugh but managed to say, "Oh shore, any ol horsetail knows that!"

He slapped Bruce on the thigh, laughing so hard Bruce wondered he did not fall off the buggy seat. Getting ahead of a "city feller" like that would put Rube in high humor for the rest of the evening, and Bruce was glad his host could feel so pleased with his own wit.

Together Rube and Bruce unhitched and unharnessed Dick and laid his harness in the buggy. When loose, Dick trotted to the hollow log watering trough. To see Dick getting his fill of pure water was almost as good as Bruce quenching his own thirst.

"Ain't you afeared a him runnin off when he's done?" Rube wondered.

"No, not Dick," Bruce assured him. "Look, he's done now. Watch him follow me into the barn. Show me his stall, will you, Rube?"

Soon Bruce could happily see and hear Dick literally smacking his lips over his oats, until he had licked up every speck, and then go after the timothy as though it were the sweetest thing he'd tasted since he was a colt suckling his mother.

"Rube, if you don't care, early in the morning I'll let him out in your pasture awhile. He sure likes it in here, though. How long you lived here, Rube?"

"Oh, bout ten years, I reckon. Come clear from Kansas."

"What brought you up the Taneum?"

"Must a been that creek over yander or else that timber never'd seen a axe back yander. Thar's a good piece a bottom in here like you see. Grows anything to eat thar nearly is. But sorter wished we'd taken up on the prairie now, clear a that creek." As Rube spoke he directed his eyes out the barn, seemingly to a young fir tree growing near the road on the schoolhouse side of the lane.

"Why is that, Rube?" Bruce asked in a concerned tone.

Looking down, Rube walked out through the barn door. Bruce followed and heard Rube say, "We gotta git up to the house fur your supper Hattie's fixed."

But when abreast of the house, Rube turned away and walked some twenty feet to a rich leafy bed of red and yellow nasturtiums. Bruce soon stood beside him. At one edge of the flowers was a smooth gray boulder a couple of feet in height with a smaller one at the opposite edge. Rube pointed at some letters chiseled into the face of the larger boulder. Bruce read:

"*Tommie Yendee, six years, 1892.* I'm sorry, Rube. Do you mean your little son fell into the creek when it was high? You couldn't save him?"

Rube nodded. "We wanted to keep him here by the fir tree, whar he played and picked them kind of flowers fur Hattie. They bud up early in the spring and she tends em, mindin how he liked em. Seems like you hanker to tell it now and again."

In the house Myra was getting acquainted with Mrs. Yendee and Rebecca. Myra had quickly noticed how clean and orderly the house was kept. On the window of her room hung a half-length, clean white curtain. On the kitchen window a hemmed flour sack hung crisply with a trace of print still on it, as though for decoration. Myra thought she had never seen a curtain do more for a window. She saw how plain and worn the chairs and tables were. Some bore signs of the homely repairs made on them, but all seemed to be serving their purpose well. She tried the two rockers and found them so comfortable it made her even like the way they creaked. The kitchen and sitting room, all in one, were just what she had expected to find way up on the Taneum. She could do her schoolwork in the tiny bedroom that would be hers at the front of the house. An airtight heating stove in the sitting room near her door would furnish heat. Through the window she could see a shed stacked to the brim with pitchy pinewood.

By the time Rube and Bruce came into the house, Hattie had supper ready for Myra and Bruce. On the blue damask tablecloth sat a bowl full of green onions, red radishes and purple-top turnips, and tiers of sliced red tomatoes on a plate. Fresh and crisp as the Taneum dawn, with a sprinkle of salt they perfectly quenched the thirsts of Myra and Bruce. Even more satisfying to them was the snowy, tangy cottage cheese, rich as the clovery bottom pasture where the cow grazed that gave it. Hattie's still-warm corn bread had the native flavor and graininess of yellow ripened corn, ground that very day. For dessert there were stewed, tender and sweet red plums that Rube had picked that morning, and only their studied politeness kept Myra and Bruce from eating all of them. It was a refreshing and restoring supper at the end of a fifteen-mile buggy ride on as hot a day as summer could bring to the Kittitas Valley.

When bedtime came, Mrs. Yendee lit the lamps. The Yendees would not let Bruce make his bed on the floor, but insisted that he sleep in Rebecca's tiny room. Rebecca could occupy a cot in their room.

Bruce said, "I'd better go out and see how Dick is before I go to bed. Myra, why don't you come along for protection? Besides, some of this fresh mountain air will help you to sleep."

"Yes," Myra agreed, "I would like to see how my new home looks in the light of the moon."

Mrs. Yendee said they would go on to bed, but that Bruce and Myra ought to see how it was in the canyon at night, as Mr. Yendee and she had done so many times themselves.

Walking toward the barn, Bruce put his arm around Myra and took her hand in his. The moonlight was reflected in her dark eyes. He wondered how he could leave her in this deep lonely canyon — so far from home and him. But he knew she would never go back to Ellensburg for long until she had fulfilled her promise to teach here. When he sighed audibly, she wondered why. They came to the barn door and went inside where Dick was rustling and chopping his hay. There was hardly any light in the barn.

Myra said softly, "It sounds good to hear Dick enjoying himself. Did he get a good drink of water, Bruce?"

"Yes, honey, he is perfectly contented now and pretty soon will be lying down there for a good night's sleep."

"I am glad of that. I hate to think how it might have been without you to bring me up here today, Bruce. I fear I shall miss you every day I am here. But I am thankful to find the Yendees are genuine people."

"Yes, Myra, I'm glad too. But won't it be too hard for you to manage the school by yourself?"

"Oh not at all, once they get to know Miss Love," Myra said with a trace of a chuckle.

His hands gently patted her back. Her arms were over his shoulders. The open barn door and window let in some light from the moon.

"Will they learn to love you too?" Bruce whispered.

"Yes," she whispered back, as Dick kept on rustling and chopping the delicious timothy.

Bruce spoke in a low, emotion-filled voice. "Sweetheart, when shall we be married?"

Myra was silent for what seemed a long time to Bruce, then slowly, softly said, "I have always wanted to have a June wedding. Would that be too soon?"

"Honey, no time could be too soon for me."

Next morning there was a reluctant parting on the

Taneum when, soon after breakfast, Bruce hitched up Dick and drove down the canyon road. To ease her sadness, Myra began at once to get the things ready she would use in school. She was glad Rebecca wanted to go to the schoolhouse with her. There would be much cleaning to do before school opened on the following day. The room would have to be immaculate as an example to the children right from the start. This was her first school, and she wanted to make it a model that other one-room schools would want to follow. From the outside it had that appearance and she would see to it the inside was kept in good order. There was ample room in the schoolyard for the children to romp and play. She wanted the parents pleased to have her teaching their children and to earn the respect of both. Her father and aunt would be proud of her. Bruce would be, too.

For over two months now, he had been nearly always in her thoughts. She remembered how much of her life had seemed lonely before she had his company, his love. Then so soon she had to leave her paradise to come up here. But God had let her know it was His will and with His presence and help and comfort it would not be too lonely. On Saturday she would get a letter from Bruce — maybe more than one. Someone would go to Thorp and get the mail on that day. At the end of the month she could go to Ellensburg. But that seemed such a long way off. It would not be easy to wait, and except for the presence and love of God, she did not see how she could do it.

The trip back to Ellensburg gave Bruce most of the day to sit and think. He had much to think about. It seemed a long time since Myra and he had driven away from the church at Ellensburg. In that time, she had promised to marry him. That was what he came for. Already she could cook better than anyone he knew, and her housekeeping was the best. Very fortunate would be the children whose mother was Myra, his wife. If only he could be a father worthy of her. His religion was in no way what hers was, but he didn't want her to know that. It would make her feel bad. So he would always go to church and even to prayer meeting with her. Her father and aunt would like that, too. Those other girls couldn't compare with Myra. It was too bad he had not met Myra sooner. She was so ravishing with her dark eyes and wealth of glossy, dark brown hair. It was a wonder that someone had not beaten him to her, especially when he didn't at all deserve her. Perhaps he could make up for that. Anyway, he would try very hard to. If only Dick there could know how concerned she was for him. "Let him take it easy, won't you, Bruce?" she said. But maybe old Dick did hear that, seeing that he never misses anything.

Why'd she ever come up here on this Taneum? Any school would have hired her. It's good she thinks those Yendees are all right. Probably neither one of them ever got into the third grade in school. All they know is work and sweat, seven days a week. You have to milk cows on the Fourth of July even. I'd hate to be stuck up there when that snow gets deep like they say it does. But that doesn't faze Myra. Just imagine her being snowbound with Yendees very long. Her English is pure as an English professor's, but they use the word "hain't" as though it had a college education. Probably by the time she gets through with them, it will have. Rebecca is in the eighth grade, and already speaks nearly like a schoolmarm. Wonder what kind of other kids Myra will have in school? All I can say is they'd better mind. Every last one of them will learn a lot from her. She won't have it any other way, unless they're not all there. There's that big pine we stopped to look at. It's lonely coming by here without her.

On Saturday morning, at the end of the fourth week of school, Myra rode with the Yendees in their spring wagon down to Thorp in time to catch the noon train to Ellensburg. She would return Sunday evening on the five o'clock train. The Yendees would meet her. The train trip cost twenty-five cents, and she paid Mr. Yendee fifty cents, making it too expensive to go home more often than every four weeks. But her infrequent visits made them all the more eagerly awaited and happy occasions. Bruce, with Dick, always met her at the Ellensburg depot on Saturday and took her back there Sunday evening. The time in between was a delight to her as she hoped it was to Bruce. The church service on Sunday morning seemed like perfect blessedness. The charm of the ice cream parlor and her memory of the happy times there with Bruce on Saturday evening would keep her company in the weeks ahead.

At the drugstore, Bruce waited on many customers in a day. Myra knew some of them would be attractive single girls, but she never doubted his devotion to her was as genuine and deep as hers was to him. And where before Bruce would have flirted carelessly with the other girls, he now cultivated a more businesslike, but friendly attitude, as much with one customer as with the other.

It was in this manner that he greeted a barely grown girl coming into the drugstore one morning at eleven, only five weeks after Myra had opened her school on the Taneum. The girl had a prescription written by Dr. Robeson. Her name was Alice Smith. Bruce quickly began to measure out and compound the prescribed ingredients. By the time the transaction was completed, Bruce thought he had detected in the girl's shy repeated glances a purpose to get better acquainted with him. He would not have cared for her —

even before he'd fallen in love with Myra. For although Alice was pretty enough, girls like her seemed too immature and frivolous to Bruce. Myra suited him.

The next morning at eleven, Alice again came tripping into the drugstore where Bruce was alone working on the stock. This time she did not have a prescription to be filled. She seemed enveloped in a delicate cloud of perfume that Bruce guessed she was trying out for the first time. She flashed him an open smile rather than shyly glancing at him as she walked over to the fountain counter and sat on a stool.

Bruce took his place back of the counter, saying, "What will you have this morning?"

"Oh, I guess I'll have a strawberry soda," Alice replied, smiling.

Bruce squirted the flavoring into a glass, then drew enough soda water to fill it. He set it in front of Alice. Bruce wanted to return to his stock work, but she made him feel that would be rude.

"This is just what I needed," Alice cooed as she rolled her eyes up at Bruce.

"Glad you like it."

"You know *my* name, what's yours?"

"Oh, everyone calls me Bruce . . . . You can, too."

"When do you get time to eat?"

"Right now! Here comes Mr. Young. If you want any more soda he'll get it for you. I have to go in the back for a minute."

Bruce walked away, but feeling that he didn't want to. What's got wrong with me, he thought. I hope she gets out of here before I do. I don't like her looking at me.

When Bruce came back through the store, ready to go out, he was glad to see Alice had gone — as he hoped — to stay. Telling Mr. Young he would be back in two hours, Bruce hurried out to the sidewalk and walked toward the

City Cafe. He had to work until eleven that evening, but now he would have time to play some pool. He hadn't let Myra know how he liked to play pool.

That girl tried to be friendly with him. She did look pretty. Better than most who came into the store. She sure knew how to put on the right perfume for a fresh sunny morning. She's nothing but a kid. I'm glad she got out of there. Oh, oh, here she is, coming round the corner.

Alice greeted him, "Hello, Bruce. I was going down to see the train come in, but guess I won't. Didn't have nothing else to do, it seemed like. Where you going?" She smiled hopefully at him.

"The City Cafe. It's time for me to eat."

"I go right by there going home," Alice said.

So they walked together toward the City Cafe. That was nothing. It wasn't nothing, though, when they got to the City Cafe, and Bruce didn't stop and go inside.

Bruce never doubted he was in love with Myra, but Alice was there beside him exuding sweet odors. Bruce never could disappoint anyone, and he felt now it would be despicable for him to disappoint a pretty girl.

After Bruce and Alice had walked a few blocks, she stopped and pointed at a small square house in need of paint.

"That's where I live," she said. "My little brother and sister are at school. Papa is working down at the roundhouse. How about me and you fixing something to eat?" Bruce followed Alice into her house.

Alice's father was a hostler at the roundhouse. Two years before, her mother had died, so Alice had to keep house for the family. It had been a lonely life for her, but now she had Bruce's company and sympathy. She would have the same on other days, giving her more happiness and making Bruce glad, on those days, he had met her. He had to tell

Alice he was engaged to be married. For him not to tell her
would have been unfair. There was no need of Myra knowing. He would write her every week, and whenever she was
in Ellensburg he would be most attentive. Alice would
understand how that was. Bruce liked that about Alice. She
was understanding. Probably more than Myra would be if
she knew.

A few days before Christmas, Myra could come home to
stay for two weeks. Her anticipation had been almost sub-
lime, surmounting the challenge and interest she got from
teaching on the Taneum. She had learned to appreciate the
congeniality and worth of those known in town as simple
people. She was glad she still had more than four months to
live and work with them. Eager as she was to begin her
married life, she hoped that waiting would help to give
Bruce and her the maximum appreciation for each other.

Myra's time at home was anxiously awaited by Bruce.
Dreaming of it made it easy for him to stay away from Alice.
He hoped there would be continuous skating and sleighing.
It could be as physically invigorating and delightful as their
hours of intimate talks would be mentally. Myra had something in her head. Alice would not be of any importance
with Myra to see every day. Ever since he had seen Alice's
father in the drugstore he had been hoping she would not
mind if he quit seeing her. But it was hard to quit altogether. Myra would be of great help, at least for a couple
of weeks.

On Christmas Day, with the temperature down to freezing, it snowed until the ground was covered to a depth of
eight inches at evening. That night the temperature fell
below zero. By the next morning, the millpond was covered
with a sheet of ice that would keep on getting thicker until
the chinook wind came in February.

The first evening after Christmas, Bruce got off work at five o'clock. At seven, Myra was snuggled beside him in the cutter, covered with the buffalo robe. Her red and yellow stocking cap was pulled down over her ears. It was cold. There was no moon yet and no need for one. It could not outshine those brilliant stars close enough to reach up and touch. Dick was stepping out for all he was worth as though to keep warm. The string of bells buckled round him rang in harmony with the dozen tinkling bells jouncing on the shafts. They made a winter's symphony that only a frosty snowy arena under the stars could produce.

"I'm sure glad, honey, you got down here in time for this," Bruce said, as he leaned over close to Myra's ear.

"So am I," Myra said softly. "I never knew before how thrilling a sleigh ride could be. I hope it is still a long way to the millpond."

"Not so far," Bruce replied, "but just wait until we are gliding over that brand-new, seemingly endless ice, clear and smooth as a sheet of plate glass. We'll skate off far away from anyone. Then when we hear the near and distant crackling of the ice, we'll think it's buckling up from one end of the millpond to the other — though it's not. And I'll hug and kiss you, like this. At the bonfire on the shore, we'll see some skaters roasting marshmallows, and others there trying to warm their nearly frozen feet. The starlight piercing the crystal ice straight to the shallow mossy bottom will make us feel there's nothing between it and us. Through the clear frosty air will come the distant tones of skating blades pinging on the hard-tempered ice. See there, Myra, I had all that memorized — just for you."

"Oh, Bruce, you make me almost not want to skate rather than have to leave it afterward. That is the sad part of this. It is so hard to leave. There are only eight more days until I have to go back to teaching."

"Yes, Myra, but they'll be worth a lot. It'll be hard for me to see you have to go back up on that Taneum, though, especially with the snow so deep up there. It sort of makes me ashamed to be leading such an easy life down here. You can't imagine how happy I'll be to see you coming home to stay. . . . Well, here is where we tie up. That blanket our feet are on is to cover Dick with. I'll get it right on him."

On the millpond bank near the bonfire, Myra sat on a small log to let Bruce attach skates to her shoes. He tightened the toe clamps onto her shoe soles and buckled straps around her insteps to hold the skate heels firmly to hers. He then clamped his skates onto his shoes and buckled straps over his insteps. Wearing knit stocking caps, wool mittens and other warm clothing, they were ready to skate. Bruce took Myra's right hand in his right and her left hand in his left and began practicing with very short glides on the ice. Myra needed some support from Bruce, though she was soon able to take longer glides in time with him. Just as Bruce had said they would do, he and Myra soon had skated to the far bank of the millpond. Myra thought nothing could be so slippery and hard as the ice, that nothing so thick and solid could be so transparent. It gave her a light airy feeling as though floating in a dream, but that only made her want more of it.

"What is that sound?" she said in alarm to Bruce.

"Oh, it's just the ice stretching and yawning while lapping up this cold snap. Honey, it's nothing to worry about. The ice won't break. But it gives me an excuse to put my arms around you. Isn't this cozy, away over here by ourselves where there's no mark of another skate all over this glittering ice?"

"Yes, Bruce, it is lovely here. See, they are roasting marshmallows or something way over there at the fire, and some are sitting there with their feet to it, just like you said.

And I hear the pinging of skates far away on the ice. It really *is* wonderful."

"Yes, Myra, and I hope there'll be other evenings here for us before you have to go back. Let's skate over there now and we can get in that crack-the-whip."

"That would be thrilling, I am sure," Myra said, "but the first time for me. Do you think I could keep up?"

"Oh, sure you could, honey. Hang tight to me. Let's hurry," Bruce urged.

Christmas vacation had to end, for on Sunday afternoon Myra would return to her school on the Taneum. She and Bruce rode in the buggy behind Dick over the bare pavement to the depot. The train came in on time and rolled away with the locomotive erupting quickening gusts of steam and smoke as it gradually picked up speed. Myra was aboard. It left a lump in Bruce's throat. Myra gazed out the window at the roundhouse and then at the lifeless, snow-covered fields. There was a lump in her throat, too.

The reins on Dick were slack going back to the livery stable. Bruce was thinking now more than ever that Myra was the one for him. She was so strict and particular; yet tender, warm, religious and understanding. Four weeks would be a long time for him not to see her at all. He never had enough of her cooking. Too bad all girls didn't have her taste in dress. Myra knew how to talk. But best of all was her love for children. That's the reason she's on that train now. If only someday we can have some of our own. I ought not to have been so friendly with Alice. Think what it would do to Myra — if she knew — and to me. I must have been crazy. Alice can easily find somebody better for her than me. I wonder where she got her good looks. From her mother, maybe. I can't see she had a chance of getting either good looks or sense from her father. I'll just forget to

go see her after this. She won't mind . . . probably. There
are others besides me around.

When Sunday came, Bruce went to church. There he
felt closer to Myra and thankful for the strength to keep
away from Alice all week. Faithfulness to Myra would be
easier for him in the week to come. It had all been a foolish
mistake. But from now on he'd let nothing take Myra out of
his mind. In five months they'd be married. To be faithful
until then was the least he could do.

Monday went smoothly by. Things seemed good to
Bruce. Tuesday morning he got a beautiful letter that only
Myra could write. He read it every chance he got. It was in
his inside pocket in the afternoon as he waited on Mrs.
Wade. When the front door opened, he looked up and saw
Jud Cawley, the sheriff, coming in. Mr. Young walked up
to wait on him, but Bruce thought by the motion of the
sheriff's head he must want Bruce to fill a prescription for
him. Bruce got done with Mrs. Wade and soon stood face-
to-face with the sheriff. He'd never before noticed how big
the word SHERIFF was on the star pinned to Jud's gray
mackinaw, or that his thick mustache was so long and white,
and how his neatly barbered white hair contrasted with his
black Stetson. Sheriffs usually had cold gray eyes. Funny,
Bruce hadn't noticed his before.

"Hello, Sheriff, what can I do for you?" was Bruce's
warm and friendly greeting.

"I'm afraid, Bruce, you can come with me," was the
sheriff's gentle reply.

"What do you mean, Jud?"

"I wish he hadn't, Bruce, but Smith made a complaint
against you."

"Smith! What for?"

"He claims you're the father of his daughter's unborn
baby, and she won't be eighteen for three months."

"He's crazy!"

"That may be. I hope he's wrong. Right now, Bruce, you better get your hat and overcoat. We have to go down to the office and talk it over."

The sheriff's office at the front of the jail was only about four blocks from the drugstore. Office and jail occupied the ground floor of a two-story, narrow brick building. There were other offices on the second floor. At the building entrance the sheriff motioned Bruce to go in. Bruce could hardly believe the sheriff would have him do that. He had always seen the jail there as necessary for someone else to walk into. No jail was needed for him. What had he done? Given a lonely girl a little company and affection was all. How could that be against the law? But here was the sheriff, his friend Jud Cawley, turning a heavy key in the lock of a barred door. When inside the door the sheriff closed and locked it. Bill Nelson, a deputy, was sitting in the office. Bruce had never cared for him.

"There's our padded cell," said the sheriff. "No one in there now. Next to it is a regular solitary cell. One over here, too. Had to put a prisoner in there this morning. I'll show you the tank back here."

Bruce followed the sheriff through a narrow corridor with steel bars on one side and a solid brick wall on the other. Inside the bars were bunks. Here and there a man was lying in one. Four men sat at a table playing cards. The thick tobacco smoke could not absorb the jail's staleness. Socks, shirts and drawers were hanging on the bars.

"Joe will bring some grub over in a little while from the hotel. Nothing but beans with a little fat pork and bread this time. They don't give us much to spend on them. See that blond, curly-headed fellow playing cards? He was convicted of something like they claim you did and has to do three to five years. Taking him down to the train bound for

State Prison tomorrow noon. They'll have a whole string going there. Well, let's go back to the office for a while."

"Yes, sir," Bruce said with immeasurable relief.

In the office the sheriff sat behind the desk and pointed at a chair for Bruce to sit in. To the deputy he said, "Bill, go give Joe a hand with the grub, will you? I want to talk to Bruce for a while."

"After that," Bill said, "I'll go pick up that guy at the City. He won't have nothing to eat though."

Bruce sat alone with the sheriff.

"You know, Bruce, you're in a pretty tough spot. Some of the neighbors saw you taking her home a number of times. The girl says she's sure you're the father of her unborn child. The father says he knows you are."

"That's a lie!" Bruce exploded.

"Well, Bruce, there's nothing I could do, you know . It would be up to the judge and the jury. Judge Dodd is usually pretty tough on these cases."

"What can I do, Sheriff?" Bruce asked with a deep sigh.

"They want you to marry her. Maybe you can do that, I don't know. Or you can get a lawyer in the morning. I know you could put the bond up, so I'll let you go home tonight on your word to be here at nine in the morning. Think it over good. If you marry her, they'll let you off — I think."

"Thanks, Sheriff. I'll be back here whenever you say."

On Wednesday, the local newspaper advised its readers that a marriage license had been issued to Bruce A. Calkins and Alice E. Smith. On that same day they were married in the judge's chambers. When Myra's father read about it, he was sure there'd been a mistake. But sadly enough, he soon learned that the newspaper had printed the truth about the Calkins-Smith nuptials.

Early Friday morning, Myra's father walked to the livery

stable where a team of hackneys was hitched to a bobsleigh waiting for him. He drove to the parsonage. His sister Donna, Myra's aunt, helped him pack the sleigh with bedding and food. By ten o'clock they were sledding over the snow- and ice-covered road on the way to the upper Taneum school. Their hearts were heavy. What could they say to Myra? How could they bring any consolation to her? She had been so trusting and happy. Today she would be busily teaching her pupils while rejoicing over every bit they learned, often thinking of the man she loved. But now she would have to know he was married, and they would have to tell her — no matter how hard their trip would be all the way in the cold and snow this January.

Myra opened and looked at the little gold watch hanging on a black ribbon around her neck. It was half past two and time for Rebecca's arithmetic recitation. But Rebecca was far advanced in her studies, and since it was Friday, Myra decided to read a chapter out of *Black Beauty* to the school.

In the midst of her reading, something prompted Myra to look out the window to the road. Through the falling snow she could barely make out a team and sleigh with two people in the front seat. She could not understand why it gave her such a start. But when she saw the horses turn into the schoolyard, she had to quit reading and dismiss the school.

The horses drew up and stopped at a post near the schoolhouse door where Myra stood. Yes, now she could see it was her father and her aunt who must have made a long hard drive only to see her. She should have been rejoicing to see them; instead she had a foreboding of some bad news they were bringing her. She would nevertheless try to seem overjoyed at their coming.

Myra rushed out in the snow to embrace her aunt and her father and hurry them inside where there was a blazing

hot fire in the stove. Then her father, his voice nearly breaking, had to say what had brought them. After that, nothing
was said for some time, as they all sat in plain wooden chairs
near the fire. Myra kept her eyes on the isinglass windows of
the stove door where the flames kept forming instantly dis-
appearing, orange-colored designs. Her father and aunt
watched her as though fearful of what her reaction might
be. The minutes passed.

"I am thankful to God to have both of you," Myra said
slowly, without averting her eyes from the stove. "It would
be nice to ride with you back to Ellensburg in the morning.
The Yendees would meet me at Thorp Sunday afternoon."

"Myra," Auntie said, "we would be awfully glad to have
you ride back with us. We see so little of you anymore, and
we miss you."

"Amen. We do miss you, Myra, but we have so many
blessings from God," her father murmured. "We trusted
that we could sleep here on the floor, and we brought bedding enough to make our beds. Also we have cold meat,
cheese, bread, apples and other things Auntie thought to
bring. And we brought hay for the horses. Is there a place
we can stable them overnight?"

"Of course there is. We will make you all comfortable.
You can sleep here as you have planned, but I know Mrs.
Yendee would not like it unless you came there for supper
and breakfast. Perhaps she will let you contribute whatever
you brought to make your own meals, saving enough for a
lunch tomorrow."

Later that evening, Myra's father and aunt made two
beds on the floor near the stove in the schoolhouse. A fire
was in the stove and there was plenty of pitchy pinewood
stacked nearby to keep it burning all night. On Saturday,
Mr. Yendee would stack the wood up high again inside the
room.

At the door Myra called back her loving, "Good night, Auntie and Papa."

She pulled the door tightly shut and stepped out into the snow and the night. Alone. The snow was deep in the canyon, but a path had been kept shoveled out from the road to the school. On the road, Myra walked in the track made by horses pulling bobsleds through the snow. She wore four-buckle arctics and a long wool coat and skirt. The moon shone on the spotless, fluffy snow. It was the same moon that had been so warm and sentimental that summer evening on the riverbank. Now it looked frozen — high up there in the sky. The stars were just as bright and seemed as near as ever, but they brought no comfort to Myra, walking all by herself on this night. Only a few hours ago she had been thankful that when night and sleep came she might again dream of last summer and next summer, and so awaken with wonderful memories and hopes. But how she would dread now to wake from any dreams of those summers to come. Could it be possible that all those things Auntie and Papa had read and heard were false? Surely Bruce would have told her. He had a good chance to. Myra stopped to think awhile, then shook her head. No, her Papa had gone to make sure and saw them together. Nothing could be surer for her than that. As Myra began to walk on, she slipped and fell in the soft, deep snow. Flakes fell on her face, in her eyes. For a moment she did not move, thinking if only she could cry, it would help her. No. She would have to get up someway and go on into her room.

Myra glanced at the picture of Bruce, standing all by itself on the corner shelf. She might as well leave it there. It would do no good to take it down now. She wondered what he had done with her picture. It seemed he had always been here with her as she knelt by her bed to pray and ask God's help for those less fortunate, rather than for Bruce and her-

self. But tonight, she fervently entreated God to help her.
And she asked Him as well as she could to help her to for-
give. Then she could cry. Sleep would come after while.

The ride in the bobsleigh to Ellensburg on Saturday took
most of the day. Myra, all covered with quilts, talked with
her father or aunt whenever they wanted to talk, but that
still left a lot of time to think. It was humiliating to think
how very badly she had been fooled. It tied her up inside to
think she could never again go skating with Bruce or feel
her hand in his some summer evening on the riverbank —
that he would be giving his affection to someone else. If only
she could hate him or somehow hurt him enough for that.
She would make him plenty sorry. She would find a good,
true man. And when Bruce saw how happy he was with her
and she with him, that would hurt him. Not enough
though. But it would make her feel a lot better. She had
been too good to Bruce. He didn't deserve anything good.
But then he did marry her. Good enough. Now he will get
what is coming to him. A girl like her will surely give it to
him. How could anyone be as deceitful as he had been —
or as big a fool as she? There is nothing I need do but feel
sorry for him now. So I guess that is what I'd better try to do.
Maybe it will make me feel differently than this. I hope so.

Thoughts like those kept going through Myra's mind all
the way home, for no good. They were in her mind when
she went to bed that night and would keep her awake for
hours. There would be an endless variety of them. She
would not be able to stop them. But one day they would
stop, anyway.

Hazel Wade and Myra had been friends before Myra met
Bruce. They knew many happy times together. Hazel
taught the Wayview School four miles from Ellensburg. It

happened that she saw Myra coming home in the bobsleigh this Saturday afternoon. She'd heard of Bruce's marriage. In the evening, Hazel came to see Myra. It was the friendliest thing anyone could have done for Myra, giving her the company she so needed that evening.

The next morning, Hazel was at church, too, where Myra was playing the organ in the absence of Mrs. Ames. Myra had asked her father to let her play "What a Friend We Have in Jesus" at the close of the service. After the conclusion of the hymn and benediction, Myra, with folded arms, sat looking straight ahead at an aisle seat in the fifth row. Perhaps she thought she saw someone sitting there. Then, realizing that Hazel had gone out and the church was nearly empty, she picked up her purse and handkerchief, rose from the organ bench and walked up the aisle into the vestibule.

That is the story of the minister's daughter at the age of twenty. When I met her in school at Thorp she had been teaching for many years.

Chapter 21

NUMBER 2 WHISTLED
AT MIDNIGHT

I've had a chance to sit here on the old millpond bank and read "The Minister's Daughter" again. In this perfect daylight I could read it without my glasses on. Perhaps some will read it and decide that Bruce's falseness to Myra matured her so compellingly into Miss Love the "schoolmarm." Some may think that she naturally inherited a determination to unsparingly educate children; or that she acquired it from the puritanical aunt who had helped to rear her. Others may believe that Miss Love's religious convictions persuaded her to strictly observe Biblical precepts such as: "Train up a child in the way he should go: and when he is old, he will not depart from it." Certainly she wanted to make sure that "Her children arise up, and call her blessed," as the Bible told her they should do.

Even now I might be able to throw a baseball and hit that house where Elladine and her parents lived with Miss Love. On this other side I can hear the waterfall that carried me down and over to where Miss Love stood on the bank that evening waiting for me. As much as she was tempted to teach me a lesson promptly, she put off doing it. After I was in bed that night in her house, passenger train Number 42 bowled by blowing long on its whistle. Then brakes began to squeal and grind to make it stop at Thorp. In those days there were about a dozen freight or passenger trains headed by steam locomotives each way daily.

There used to be a stagnant pond simmering over there alongside the railroad track. It was thick with slimy growth and alive with bugs and frogs. Typhoid germs dropped from passing trains lived in it, too, for I swallowed a swarm of them there one day in August. Three of us were mud crawling when John Bain sneaked up behind and smartly shoved my head down into the infested water. A mouthful of it could kill anyone and my parents were soon fearing they would lose me.

Early in September on my way to school with Frank I said I felt sick and wanted to go back home. He argued, "Aw, come on, Chub, finish out the first week in school." Frank would never claim that any later week in school meant much — but after all — "On the first week, Chub, you gotta stick out the last half-day. I sure am." But he didn't have typhoid fever, as it turned out I had. For all I knew they had to carry me home that last afternoon of the first week of school and were not to see me in school again for four months. After that, it seemed to me that the only way to be really sick was to have typhoid fever.

My parents had ordered us to stay strictly away from the pond but they had gone to see the doctor on the day I got into it. That was the summer after I was in the care of Miss Love and had chafed so at her making me stay in the yard with Elladine. Miss Love would never have let me get near that pond, though. It was to keep me out of such places that she had taken me to Tacoma for the summer.

Arlie Brown lives over there in Miss Love's old house. That looks like him on the back porch. I hope he sees me and comes over here. Yep, he's out through his gate and headed my way. I'll stand up. There, he gave me the old high sign. I'll give him the same.

"Hi yuh, Chub, never knowed you'd be out here."

"Hi, Arlie. Oh I wanted to see if the old millpond was still up here." We shook hands and tapped each other on the shoulder. Then I got back on my grassy seat as Arlie seated himself on a small barkless log facing me. He still wore faded blue bib overalls and a floppy coarse straw hat, but beneath the brim of it I could now see a few wrinkles near his eyes and mouth. Arlie reached into his front pocket, got a knife and opened it, then picked up a foot-long pine stick to whittle on. His elbows rested on his knees.

"Well, Chub, whata yuh been up to since I seen yuh?"

"Oh not much, Arlie. Been trying to make a living same as everyone, I guess."

"You got a couple of boys or so. Ain't they grown up now?"

"Yeah, they are, Arlie, so I got less mouths to feed."

"Well, Chub, I hope they didn't give you fits like you give your mom and pop them times." Arlie laughed.

"I guess I did get out a line a few times, but maybe not so much, considering some examples I had here. Not you though, Arlie. Of course there were a lot more ways of getting into things here than where my kids grew up."

"Yeah, Chub, you could think a somethin to get into anytime." Arlie laughed again. "Remember Kendall's old flour mill? You can see it over there, but it's lookin kinda shaky, ain't it? Nelson Mills's old light plant used to be next to it. Remember how it scared us, getting close to that big old dynamo. It's all gone. Probably made some cannon balls that was sent to Germany or maybe Japan along with all that sawmill machinery that's gone too."

"Arlie, we knew when that sawmill was cutting out boards and its whining and wailing were heard clear down to Thorp. Remember? After it quit running, there were a lot of short, narrow boards left in the yard nobody bought.

So dumbly enough one day, I got you to help me pull my wagon up the road half a mile to get some. We piled the wagon high with pieces of old lumber, then pulled and pushed it over that graveled road all the way to our backyard. My folks didn't notice the addition to our stock of lumber, but the owners of it, Mr. and Mrs. Mills, had seen us passing their house. After all, we hadn't thought of trying to hide it. What an embarrassment though, when I had to go in our parlor one afternoon and apologize to Mr. and Mrs. Mills for stealing their lumber. It seemed they tried their best to look like reform school owners, for my benefit."

"Yeah, Chub, we sure got in a mess now and then. But if you'd liked to fish the way I did, it would've kept you out a some trouble. I still like to fish that ol millrace down there."

"You always could catch a few trout, Arlie — even in a hole where it was hard for me to get a nibble. I used to envy you catching fish."

"Chub, remember when you and Walter Stevenson had your own company. What'd you call it?"

"W. S. & G. O. Company. That was after Frank and Bob moved away. I sure missed them."

"What'd your company do?"

"Oh, we trapped muskrats and sold a few pelts. Had a box at the post office so we wrote to all kinds of places for price lists and things like that to get some mail in our box. We tried to start a circus one time."

Being reminded of that tickled Arlie. He said, "I bet your business took a load off Miss Love's mind. I used to think you had her kinda worried sometimes. But she got a little worried about me, too — when I was in her room. She had a way a makin you learn more'n any teacher I ever knowed. She lived in that house where I'm livin now with Lloyd and family."

"Yeah, I ought to know, Arlie. I stayed there when Miss Love did. And I was in Tacoma one whole summer with her and Elladine."

"You were! I forgot that. Boy, that must've been *fun!*" Arlie exclaimed in a mock tone. "What happened?"

"Quite a bit and I would've given anything to be back here at Thorp. Imagine me then having to play with Elladine all summer. Miss Love was bound to see her and me even holding hands every place we went."

"Knowing how you were, Chub, it's a wonder you didn't run away from her."

"No, Arlie, Miss Love was not anyone an eight-year-old boy ran away from. In fact, I hardly ever got out of her sight that summer. She could be a regular old blister, as I found out, but with her religious concern for a small boy in her care she could only do him good — many folks thought. Now I have to say it too. It sure got me at first, though, when I had to call her 'Auntie.' "

"Chub, you mean you called her that?"

"I sure did and with her trying all she could to make me into some example like Elladine."

"Naw, she couldn't a done that," Arlie said, shaking his head.

"That's right. It only made me want all the more to show I wasn't that good. I guess it shows nobody can be made different than they're born to be."

"I don't know about that, Chub, but we grew up around here together and I never noticed nothin to make me think you'd spent a whole summer holdin hands with Elladine." Arlie had to laugh.

"Before you got here, Arlie, I was reading a story about Miss Love, when she was twenty. As you know, we thought she'd always been some old maid schoolmarm. But in this story she was in love with a guy named Bruce who disappointed her. I could send it to you so you could see for yourself, if you want to."

"Chub, I bet it'd be worth reading. Well, I guess I better go over and do some weeding so I can see what was planted there this spring. Stop in sometime."

"Sure, Arlie, you come to see me, too. I'm spending the night with Charles. So long now."

"So long, Chub."

That evening Charles and I sat in the sitting room where I had seen my infant brother nursing. It was where on so many cold mornings we had hurried to get behind the blazing stove while we dressed. The telephone my mother answered when I called long distance was nearby.

Charles and I were the only ones left to remember the childhood joy and pain and tears that had been there. And we recalled and talked of the neighbors who were gone. At last I saw it was almost twelve, and said to him, "Say, what time do you go to bed around here?"

"Oh, when company lets me, I reckon," he quipped, as he stood up and went into the kitchen.

When warm in bed I heard a whistle on a Milwaukee train humming through the night half a mile away. It was only a diesel but it made me think of Number 2 that used to pound over the rails only thirty yards from my bed. Called the eastbound North Coast Limited, it eased down out of the mountains about midnight, bringing welcome sounds in the still night to anyone awake in bed. There would be the far-off tones of its whistle at Ellison's crossing, and the echo bouncing back from the bluffs on both sides. As the echo faded away, there came the click-clacking of steel wheels bounding over rail joint gaps and the rapid rhythmic sounds of piston rods driving the steam exhaust up the smokestack. Like band music heard above the wind, those sounds could soon put to sleep anyone in bed listening. But in a matter of seconds, Number 2 with shrilling whistle pulled wide open would flash past Thorp at ninety miles an hour, quivering our beds. Then, as stealthily as it had come, the sound of steam escaping and of steel clanking on steel would fade off down the track toward the river bend. The only sounds still to hear then were of the operator's footsteps going out to bring in the sack of mail thrown off of Number 2 and of him, when back inside the depot, closing the door. Then it was time in Thorp to go back to sleep until morning.